ORCHID PESTS AND DISEASES

Series Editor James B. Watson

American Orchid Society
Education. Conservation. Research.

2008 *Revised Edition*

American Orchid Society
Delray Beach, Florida

American Orchid Society

Contents

 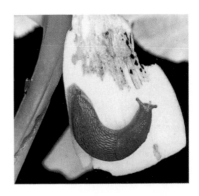

Front Cover (left to right) Black rot on *Cattleya*; snail on *Rhynchosophrocattleya* (syn. *Brassolaeliocattleya*) Pollyana; mealybugs on leaf (inset); freak flowers of *Cattleya labiata* (inset); virus-marred *Rhynchosophrocattleya* (syn. *Brassolaeliocattleya*) Pamela Hetherington flower (bottom right).

Back Cover (top to bottom) Boisduval scale on pseudobulb; aphids on flower stems; caterpillar on petal.

Title Page Virus-marred *Rhynchosophrocattleya* (syn. *Brassolaeliocattleya*) flower; black rot on *Cattleya*.

All cover and title page photographs by Greg Allikas, except photograph of mealybugs on leaf by Charles Marden Fitch.

Opposite Boisduval scale on *Cattleya* leaf (left); slug on orchid flower (right).
Photographs by Charles Marden Fitch.

Orchid Pests and Diseases ©2008 American Orchid Society, 16700 AOS Lane, Delray Beach, Florida 33446-4351 (telephone 561-404-2000; fax 561-404-2100; e-mail TheAOS@aos.org; Web site www.aos.org). Library of Congress Catalog Card Number 2001 132032. ISBN 0-923096-13-2. The opinions and recommendations that may appear in this publication regarding the selection and use of specific plant-care products, including but not limited to pesticides, fungicides and herbicides, are those of the individual authors, and not those of the American Orchid Society, which neither adopts nor endorses such opinions and recommendations and disclaims all responsibility for them. When selecting and using such products, readers should seek and obtain the advice of the manufacturer and of responsible government agencies. 08.01.5M

Physiological Disorders of Orchids
By Thomas J. Sheehan, PhD

O RCHIDS ARE DISTRIBUTED worldwide and come from a vast array of habitats. In addition, because of their diverse nature, they require special cultural care to thrive in a greenhouse or other indoor situation. Orchid plants are subject not only to insects, diseases and viruses, but also to a number of ailments called physiological disorders. Some physiological disorders may be limited to a small group of genera or species while others are more widespread. When seeking the cause of a problem, the first possibilities to check are for diseases or insects. If these are proven not to be the cause, then it may be physiological. Detection is not always easy because some physiological disorders, such as mesophyll cell collapse (see page 21) of phalaenopsis leaves, have symptoms that resemble those of certain orchid viruses. Often the virus is considered the causal organism when, in fact, it is not. Great care must be exercised in making determination regarding the cause of a problem because the wrong remedy might be applied — to the detriment of the plant. In general, most physiological problems are distinct enough to be separated from either disease or insect damage.

Water

It often has been stated that more orchids are killed from improper watering that by any other cause. There are some who will go even a step further and say "than all other factors combined." Those are both strong statements. Unfortunately, they are true, because water and watering methods are responsible for many problems.

The average orchid greenhouse will house a number of different genera and species, usually both terrestrial and epiphytic plants, and pots of a variety of sizes will be present. The epiphytes may be growing in pots (clay, plastic or even ceramic); on tree-fern plaques or cork slabs; or in hanging baskets. Immediately two or three potential problems can arise. If the grower has a combination of plastic and clay pots, how can plants be watered uniformly? Plants in clay pots, for example, dry out faster than those in plastic pots. Therefore, a watering frequency for plants in clay pots is unsuitable for those in plastic, possibly causing root damage.

When an orchid exhibits atypical symptoms, do not always assume it is ill. Understanding a plant's life cycle helps to determine if a condition is natural. Here, normal physiological breakdown of *Liparis* (syn. *Malaxis*) *latifolia* at the end of the growing season might cause the grower to think the plant is dying. However, it is natural for this deciduous species to lose leaves.

A healthy root system, as in the case of this *Catasetum pileatum*, is necessary for any orchid to make use of the water it is given.

Watered too frequently immediately after repotting, this cattleya hybrid lost its roots and rhizome to black rot. By then, it was too late to save the plant.

Plants mounted on cork slabs and potted in moss-lined baskets in the same area challenge the grower to develop a watering regime that meets the needs of both without causing some to be overwatered or underwatered.

If there is more than one medium, then another problem is encountered. Each medium dries out at a different rate and must be watered accordingly. A third potential problem is the location of the plants in the greenhouse. A plant in a hanging basket dries out faster than a similar plant in the same medium in a pot on a greenhouse bench. A tree-fern plaque or cork slab obviously will dry faster than a hanging basket. It is then clear that the usual variety of containers and media used in the average greenhouse invites problems.

There are two other factors to consider in discussing water:

■ The quantity required.

■ The quality of the water used.

There are probably more problems caused by quantity than quality because plants are frequently overwatered.

Quantity of Water Plants should be watered thoroughly by applying moisture to the surface of the medium until it runs out the bottom of the container, then should not be watered again until the surface of the medium is dry to the touch. This is especially true if the medium has a very high water-holding capacity, such as one containing mostly peat moss. If the surface is not permitted to dry out between waterings, the orchid's roots may be deprived of oxygen, and this could be detrimental to overall growth. For example, a medium with high moisture-holding capacity that is kept too wet may have some oxygen in the capillary water, but it may not be sufficient to sustain the roots. By allowing some drying out, the air in the medium is exchanged, and the oxygen is enriched within. Plants in the wild, especially epiphytes, have their roots almost totally exposed to the atmosphere, where air exchange is no problem. These exposed roots also experience drying out from time to time, too. Thus, allowing the surface of the potting medium to dry helps duplicate conditions that exist in the wild.

It is true that plants that are under watered also suffer and may be damaged

Without live roots, this paphiopedilum is incapable of absorbing the water it so desperately needs. Note the symptoms of severe desiccation.

Correct watering is essential for normal growths to develop. Here, inadequate moisture caused a developing growth of *Trichopilia suavis* to develop accordion pleating. Adjusting the watering schedule will not undo this damage, but it will enable future growths to develop naturally.

beyond recovery. Drying out can result from infrequent waterings, but it also can occur if the medium used has a poor water-holding capacity or lacks the ability to retain water. Because most orchid media contain copious amounts of organic matter, they usually have adequate water-retention potential. However, when some organic matter dries out, it is difficult to rewet. Water applied to the surface may pass right through the pot without wetting the medium, a condition especially true when barks or peat moss are dominant components of the medium. If this is allowed to continue, the roots will die and the plants will shrivel up. The damage may look the same as that from overwatering, which also kills the roots. Dry media can be rewetted by several waterings. First, the medium should be watered lightly, allowed to stand for approximately one hour, then given a heavy watering. Occasionally, a third watering may be required to rewet the medium completely. Some growers say they can accomplish the same thing by using a fine spray of water over the plants. The mistlike particles settle on the medium and gradually rewet it. Submerging the pot briefly will wet the medium quickly, but some media,

such as bark and tree fern, may float out of the pot and need to be secured somehow. Once the medium has been conditioned, it then will start absorbing water normally.

Water Quality Today, most growers using city water supplies do not have to be too concerned about the quality of their water because federal regulations governing drinking water are well within tolerances considered good for orchids. Individuals with private wells should have their water analyzed at least yearly to be sure it is not deteriorating. This is especially true along coastal areas, where salt intrusion can be a serious problem. There also are fewer problems in areas where the annual rainfall is more than 40 inches (100 cm).

The problem encountered most frequently is that of high soluble salts. Fortunately, the total soluble-salt content of any water system is easily measured by a simple electric conductivity test. It is easy to determine, and the test can be completed in a very short time, possibly within less than 10 minutes. Municipal water departments are constantly running tests, so that a salt reading is available and usually can be found out on line or by a phone call. Soluble-salt tests often are available at county agricultural extension offices, boards of health or even sometimes at city water plants.

The test results are usually expressed in mhos (siemans, units of electrical conductivity in the interrational system, equal to 1 ampere per volt). A report given in mhos can be converted to parts per million (ppm) by multiplying the mhos whole number by seven, which will give the approximate ppm. For instance, $25 \times 10_{-5}$ mhos would convert to $25 \times 7 = 175$ ppm. Using this method of analysis, water for orchids can be classified as follows:

When water high in soluble salts collects and then evaporates on orchid leaves, residues of those salts remain. Here, water drawn from a well causes unsightly whitish deposits.

- Less than $25 \times 10_{-5}$ — the best (less than 175 ppm)
- $25–75 \times 10_{-5}$ — good (175 to 525 ppm)
- $75–125 \times 10_{-5}$ — use with caution (525 to 875 ppm)
- More than $125 \times 10_{-5}$ — find a new water source (more than 875 ppm)

It would be simple if all laboratories reported in the same terms, but this is not always the case. Some water analysis reports will be expressed as millimhos, centimillimhos or even micromhos. Usually the laboratory will convert any of these electric conductive expressions to mhos or ppm on request.

In addition to the problems of high-saline water building up salts in the orchid-growing medium, the salts can present another difficulty. If this water is used in overhead watering systems or to syringe foliage, it will leave salt deposits on foliage, stems and even exposed roots. This salt buildup also can be detrimental to growth. (See section on hard water below for explanation of salt deposits on leaves.) Consequently, applying water with a high salt content to plants from above should be avoided. It also should be pointed out that if it is necessary to use water with high salt concentrations, switch the plants to nonporous containers. Plastic pots usually produce better results when compared with porous clay pots when plants grown in both are irrigated with high-salt water. The porous pots absorb and hold the salts whereas the plastic pots will not.

Hard Water Another condition facing growers is hard water. Such water has a relatively high concentration of either calcium or magnesium salts, yet otherwise is considered to be usable for orchids. Some people consider water to be hard if it has 150 ppm of calcium carbonate ($CaCO_3$), yet there are reports of people's successfully using water having 300 ppm of $CaCO_3$ for orchids. Although such water is not usually satisfactory for bathing or laundry, it is usable for orchids as long as the water is kept off the leaves. Syringing the leaves with hard water will leave a calcareous residue on them, eventually covering much of the surface, reducing

7

Salt deposits in a medium can impact an orchid's ability to take root and grow. Roots of this mounted *Trichoceros antennifer* are especially sensitive to the salt deposits in the tree-fern totem, burning at the tips and refusing to take hold.

available light and slowing growth. There are times when hard water actually can be beneficial. In those situations where the medium (especially one rich in peat moss) is very acid or when an acid-base fertilizer is being used, then hard water may help to prevent acid residue from building up in the medium. At the same time, it also supplies calcium, which the plants may need.

For the grower with a hard-water problem, there is a solution, and that is to consider a water softener. However, be careful when choosing one because some of the softeners on the market today soften the water by exchanging sodium for the calcium and magnesium salts, which results in water with a higher electric conductivity. Because most commercial softeners are designed for laundry purposes, the sodium is acceptable. Unfortunately, water with a high sodium content can be detrimental — even highly toxic — to orchids. Plants irrigated with water softened in such a manner often absorb excessive amounts of sodium, resulting in root injury or in a blackening of the tips of cat-

tleya leaves. Water in many areas has small amounts of sodium, but this is not a problem with orchids as long as there are adequate levels of calcium present. It should be pointed out that both calcium and magnesium are essential elements for plant growth, and their presence helps to improve orchid growth. Therefore, hard water may be preferable for orchids rather than water supplied by some of the commercial water softeners.

In some cases, hard water and water with a high pH can be treated with dilute acids to lower the pH to between 5.5 and 6.5. At these pH levels, water does not leave insoluble residues on the foliage. It also prevents salts from accumulating in the medium because they are readily removed by leaching. If the decision is made to use weak acid treatments, use only plastic pipes. If the system has galvanized or copper pipes, the weak acid will act as a solvent and can release enough zinc from the galvanized pipes to cause zinc toxicity symptoms on the orchid plants. Copper also can be released, and it, too, can be detrimental.

There are also a number of resinous units that "demineralize" water and can be used when the water is hard and also high in soluble salts. These units can remove enough impurities so that the water can be used safely on orchids because the end product, depending on the unit, may be similar to distilled water. Unfortunately, the initial cost of this type of demineralizer is relatively high, while operating costs may be lower. The latter will depend almost entirely on the type of water being treated and the quantity of soluble salts that have to be removed. Many industries as well as orchid growers use this type of purifier. Reverse-osmosis systems also can be used.

Rainwater It often has been suggested to orchid growers with water problems that they collect rainwater and use it, the theory being that "rainwater is the purest type of water there is." Perhaps when our early ancestors trod this planet, that was true. Today, however, it is not necessarily so. In the wild, where orchids are found growing on trees in tropical forests, they are bathed in rainwater that has collected nutrients and other materials from the leaves above the orchid plants. Actually, these are impurities that help to sustain plant growth and are not necessarily detrimental. However, in many industrial areas today, rainwater may be laced with chemicals, and the resulting precipitation may be on the acid side. Although rainwater from one area may be quite different from that in another place, most rainwater is as pure — if not purer — than most tap water.

In many areas, rainwater is collected and used for irrigating orchids all year. In this kind of situation, close attention should be paid to the type of storage container used as well as the surface on which the water is collected. Galvanized surfaces or surfaces coated with chromium, tar and tarlike products, or other toxic preservatives should be avoided. Once the water is collected, it should be kept as clean as possible. Avoid recollecting or letting runoff from greenhouse irrigation return to the holding tank. Runoff water is apt to be contaminated and could contaminate the entire tank and render the water useless. The introduction of deleterious fungi or bacteria could cause serious disease problems, not to mention the salt problems that could develop from fertilizer runoff getting into the tank.

Light

A second important cultural problem area with orchids is light. The most critical question is just how much light the plants should receive for maximum growth and flowering. The answer to this question would be simple if only one type

When adding orchids to a collection, evaluate the environment and choose those recommended for available light conditions. Doing so increases the plants' chances of flowering and reduces future physiological problems. Hobbyists in South Florida, Hawaii and elsewhere where bright light prevails, for example, often grow vandas and their relatives, which includes *Ascocenda* Jacky Begaud, shown here.

of orchid were cultivated in a growing area. However, most growers, whether commercial or hobbyist, cultivate a wide variety of genera and species, many of which differ greatly in light requirements. Frequently they are all grown in one greenhouse. Some orchids, such as some vandas, can grow in full sun, whereas others, such as phalaenopsis, grow best at much lower light intensities. Thus, the range of light needed can run from a low of 10 to 15 percent to a high of 100 percent of full sunlight. The total amount of sunlight varies, with extreme differences from place to place around the world. For example, in summer in Florida, light intensity can be as high as 15,000 foot-candles — about 10 times the amount recommended for phalaenopsis (1,500 foot-candles) or five times that required for cattleyas (3,000 foot-candles). Fortunately, orchids are adaptable and can be grown under a considerable range of light intensities without excessive damage to the plants. Also, there are differences between light requirements for plants grown under glass and those grown in the open or under shade. Therefore, it is necessary to generalize on some of the problems encountered with light and its effects on orchid plants.

It was stated that vandas grow in full sun. Although that statement is true for certain tropical areas, it does not necessarily mean that it will be true all over. For example, the same vanda hybrid that can be grown in a field in full sun in Singapore with no adverse effects may show a severe case of leaf burn when grown in a clear glass greenhouse. It will all depend on the temperature within the greenhouse and whether or not the heat is easily dissipated from the greenhouse and/or the plant's leaves, as it would be by the trade winds in the tropics. A variety of factors (greenhouse temperature, humidity, air movement) play important roles as far as the plant's tolerance to light is concerned. Many small greenhouses lack fans to circulate air, nor do they have any form of air cooling or conditioning. In such a situation, even cat-tleyas will experience injury if exposed to light intensities more than 4,000 foot-candles for an extended period of time. Phalaenopsis exposed to full sun after growing at 1,500 foot-candles will show extensive leaf burn in less than 30 minutes. Most of the damage will occur on those leaves that are perpendicular to the sun's rays. Cattleyas can be grown in full sun — but under a misting system — and show no light injury. They will flower well, but the leaves may be almost purple in color. Some genera, such as *Cymbidium*, will grow in full sun as long as there is good air movement to keep the leaves cool.

A problem may occur in autumn and winter when a cymbidium is grown at low temperatures (50 F, 10 C) at night and then exposed to full sun first thing in the morning. Under such circumstances, plants often develop crippled flowers. This is especially true if the weather has been cloudy for several days and then the morning dawns bright and clear. The plants heat up rapidly and transpire moisture faster than the roots can supply it. Thus, the flower buds, which are the most tender part of the plant, are the first to suffer and crippling often ensues. A good sign of high light intensities, below injurious levels, is yellowing of the older foliage and shriveling of the older pseudobulbs. Only the newest growths are unaffected.

Fortunately, light is relatively easy to control. Because most orchids grow under lower light intensities, the amount of light entering a greenhouse can be reduced. Shading the greenhouse is the most effective method of reducing light intensity. It also gives the benefit of reducing the amount of heat entering the greenhouse or shade house where plants are growing.

Light and Heat There is a direct relationship between the amount of light and heat in a greenhouse. If a white shading compound is used to coat the top of the greenhouse, the temperature is reduced as the light intensity is reduced. The absorptive powers of shading compounds vary with color, and some colors absorb more heat than white. If a color other than white is used, check its absorptive characteristics because some of those that absorb copious amounts of heat may reradiate some of that heat to the plants.

There is a direct relationship between high light and high temperature, and their effects in the greenhouse are often confused. In most cases, orchid plants are capable of growing and flowering under higher light intensities than quoted in the literature — as long as the excessive heat generated at these intensities is dissipated effectively. Today, with the installation of evaporative cooling units, plants can grow under moderately excessive light intensities because the air temperature is reduced by the cooling devices. These devices not only reduce the air temperature but also increase the air movement, which has additional cooling effects. It is obvious, then, that an orchid plant's tolerance to light is variable and depends on a number of other cultural parameters.

Inadequate Light If the light received by an orchid plant is too low, other problems arise. Although orchid plants will often continue to grow under dense shading or during periods of low light intensities (such as in areas where cloud cover is prevalent throughout much of the year), the foliage is usually dark green, and the new growths are weak and spindly. Frequently, the growths produced under these conditions are "blind" so flowering is greatly reduced or eliminated altogether.

Sometimes plants exposed to high night temperatures have spindly growth habits similar to heavily shaded plants. However, they can be distinguished because the leaves are usually the normal green and not the dark green of the low-light plants. Plants exposed to these conditions also often produce blind leads. If the light intensity is high along with high night temperatures, then the leaf color will be lighter green.

Artificial Light The grower who cultivates plants indoors under artificial light is faced with an entirely different set of problems. However, many orchid plants can be grown satisfactorily in such a setup once some problems are addressed. The most important problem is the selection of plants to grow under such a regime. Plants that normally grow in heavy shade and are of relatively small stature are the best choices. Selecting plants that are near equal heights at maturity is a better choice than selecting a combination of large plants and miniatures. A mixture of sizes

Homeowners who cultivate orchids on the windowsill need to take precautions to ensure plants reach their full potential. Without rotation, this windowsill-grown cattleya has developed a lopsided appearance.

Orchids make great companion plants to African violets, as shown in this light-garden set-up in a New York apartment. Positioning the orchids on risers of various heights places the tops of most of the plants an equal distance from the tubes. Pots of assorted sizes are an alternative to the risers shown here.

can only lead to problems because the light intensity under a bank of lamps varies inversely as the square of the distance from the lamps increases. If the lights have to be raised to clear a tall plant (a vanda, for example), then the light reaching the miniature on the shelf is greatly reduced. There have been reports of cymbidiums grown under lights, but usually the results are not as satisfactory as they would be for growing phalaenopsis or paphiopedilums.

It is relatively easy to provide sufficient light to grow the shade-tolerant plants, but to get enough light for plants normally grown in full sun is difficult. As light intensities increase, so does heat, and it is difficult to dissipate heat inside the house.

Fluorescent tubes produce 1,000 to 1,800 foot-candles of light without elaborate lighting devices. This is about 10 percent of the average light at noon most of the year. However, in order to obtain this level, plants must be within 6 inches of the lamps. As mentioned, phalaenopsis

Orchids that normally grow in shade and are of relatively small stature are the best choices for growing under lights. However, some that require bright light to flower, like this *Potinara* Cherub, will also succeed under lights.

and paphiopedilums will grow well under these conditions because all the leaves will be near the lights. But having a tall plant dispersed among them would greatly alter the intensity. The lights should remain on for at least 12 hours daily. Some growers operate lights 16 hours. If plants are exposed only to artificial light, a combination of fluorescent and incandescent lights is needed to ensure robust growth as fluorescent lights are stronger in the "cool" colors (blue) and incandescent lights are stronger in the "warm" colors (red). It generally is recommended to use two 40-watt incandescent bulbs for every four 40-watt fluorescent tubes used. This combination is sufficient to serve a 4 × 4 foot area. There is also a variety of high-intensity lights that produce less heat and are good for indoor use.

According to the late Dr. O. Wesley Davidson, there are a number of problems peculiar to orchids grown under lights:

- Weak growth and no flowers — caused by insufficient light.
- Weak, shriveled and stunted growth — caused by extremely dry atmosphere in the house.
- Failure to flower and weak growth — caused by high temperatures encountered while the lights are on. Cool white fluorescent tubes give off much less heat than incandescent bulbs.
- Failure to flower but good growth — caused by light being on too long for plants that normally flower under short-photoperiods.

It is best to check light by using a light meter. Once a reading is obtained, either move the plants closer to or farther away from the lights to get the right intensity. If the maximum intensity is below 1,000 foot-candles, it can be corrected by extending the light period from 12 to 14 or 16 hours or longer so that the plants will have the equivalent of 12,000 foot-candles per day (1,000 foot-candles × 12 hours).

Another problem encountered is that some orchids are photoperiodic responders, and their flowering is controlled by the length of the day. Most are short-day plants, flowering in the autumn, when days are becoming shorter. Weak lights (low intensities) and extending the day length (14 to 16 hours) can prevent those photoperiodic plants from flowering. They will continue to produce vegetative growths and look good but will never flower. *Cattleya trianaei* is a good example. As a matter of fact, it is possible to flower *C. trianaei* plants twice a year just by manipulating the day length. *Cattleya trianaei, Cattleya labiata* and their hybrids are relatively easy to manipulate as far as flowering is concerned, whereas *Cattleya warscewiczii* (syn. *Cattleya gigas*) is not.

The yellowing leaves of this recently repotted paphiopedilum seedling indicate a possible nitrogen deficiency.

Temperature Temperature in the home also can be a problem. In those situations where the temperature is high and the light intensity low, there is a greater chance of blind growths developing. Under these same conditions, the new growths are softer, more spindly and more apt to be blind. Under normal growing conditions, the temperature outdoors drops at night, yet the temperature in the house may not be lowered more than a few degrees. Consequently, some of the temperature problem could be eliminated by lowering the temperature at night. Plants growing under lights at 70 to 80 F (21 to 26.5 C) can stand 55 to 60 F (13 to 15.5 C) at night and excellent growth will result. Most commercial growers try to run their greenhouses 10 to 15 F (5.5 to 8.3 C) cooler at night after clear days and 5 to 10 F (2.7 to 5.5 C) cooler at night after a cloudy day. There will be some exceptions to this, considering the vast size of the orchid family and the myriad climatic situations under which orchids are found in their native habitats. Growing or learning to grow a wide vari-ety of genera and species under lights indoors may require a great deal of trial and error, but each species successfully added to the collection will make it worthwhile.

Nutritional Problems

Because most orchids are grown in potting mixtures relatively rich in organic matter and are fertilized frequently, nutrient deficiencies are seldom seen in either commercial or amateur collections. As the organic matter decomposes, it releases nutrients to the substrate, which then are used by plants in their growth cycle. Additional nutrients also may be supplied by the water. The amount and elements vary, depending on the source of the water. Because there are great variations in the nutrients supplied by the potting medium, the water supply and the requirements of the plants being grown, the medium and water supply, in some cases, may provide sufficient nutrients to produce good growth. However, should the potting medium and water be lacking in any of the essential elements needed for plant growth, then the plant may exhibit signs of nutrient deficiency. In general, this is the exception.

Problems of overfertilization or calcium deficiency are more common than any other nutrient problem. Overfertilization often occurs because of a grower's lack of understanding of orchid culture. An orchid plant is approximately 90 percent water, and only two percent is composed of mineral elements. These essential elements are furnished by fertilizer, medium and water. Most orchids require small concentrations of mineral elements to ensure good growth. Unfortunately, some growers believe that if one pound of fertilizer is recommended, two pounds will be better. The end result is that plant growth is inhibited and, as soluble salts build up in the medium, they may even burn the roots, further inhibiting growth. Growers who have water that is high in soluble salts should be especially careful when fertilizing because overfertilization could have disastrous results.

The safest way to fertilize orchids is to use liquid fertilizers. Dry fertilizers are much more difficult to apply uniformly, and, if they are readily soluble, they may cause damage to the tender exposed roots. Liquid fertilizers are easier to apply, and the fertilizer is distributed throughout the pot and is more readily available to the roots. Also, any liquid fertilizer applied either accidentally or intentionally to the foliage will be taken up through the leaves. Some growers routinely fertilize their orchids by foliar application. When using this method, it is a good practice to fertilize one day and wash the leaves off the next. Doing this prevents the growth of algae on the plants, which could have a detrimental effect on plant growth. Plastic-coated, slow-release fertilizers also can be used for orchids. Growers often use them as a supplement to their liquid fertilization program. Be careful using manures, whether fresh or dehydrated. The former is high in ammonia, and the latter may contain high concentrations of sodium chloride (table salt), both of which can be damaging if not used as directed.

Calcium Deficiency Calcium deficiency is most evident on cattleyas, paphiopedilums and other orchids during the spring and summer months, when the plants are in active growth. Young, expanding leaves start turning black at the tips, and as the blackening spreads downward onto the leaf blade, it is preceded by a yellow "halo." In severe cases, it may encompass the entire leaf blade. In *Cattleya*, it also can cause a complete blackening and death of the developing leaf. This malady is most apt to occur when the calcium level in the leaf drops below 1.4 percent. If leaf calcium remains above 2 percent, no symptoms will develop. Unfortunately, several fertilizers used by orchid growers do not have any calcium-based units in them, thus calcium must be added to the medium to alleviate the problem. A light dusting of lime over the surface of the medium usually will suffice. This deficiency is highly variable and may show up on one cattleya clone with almost all the new leaves turning black, while plants of the same clone next to it appear perfectly normal.

Calcium deficiency is sometimes overlooked because it has been called sunburn (it occurs during warm weather) or it is confused with the damage caused by the excessive use of dry fertilizer. An overfertilized cattleya will first have blackening of the younger foliage (not just the new leaf, as in calcium deficiency) and possibly some of the older leaves as well. In severe cases, root injury and the death of the plant may ensue.

Whenever a plant has been overfertilized accidentally, the best remedy is to flush as much of the salts out of the pot as quickly as possible, thereby minimizing the damage. Apply large amounts of water to the pot, allowing it to run out the bottom. It is best to flush it several times over several hours to eliminate the salts. An application of 6 inches of water to a 6-inch pot, in several applications, depending on the medium, could leach out as much as 50 percent of the soluble salts in the pot.

Potting Faults

Correct potting at the proper time of year can be an important factor in ensuring good growth in the absence of any other limiting cultural factor.

Most potting problems can be solved by determining when to repot and how often to repot.

For sympodial orchids, such as *Cattleya* and *Encyclia*, it is best to repot right after flowering or just as roots begin to emerge from the new lead. By selecting a pot of the proper size, the plants should not need to be repotted more frequently than every two years. Monopodials, such as *Vanda* and *Phalaenopsis*, can be repotted any time they are in active growth. They need not be repotted more frequently than once every two years. Sometimes growers do not repot monopodials until they become too tall and the pot no longer can support the plant.

By following these few rules, good growth should ensue because the new roots will penetrate the medium rapidly, with minimal mechanical damage, and are less apt to become a meal for a cockroach or snail.

Dividing Orchids Repotting is an excellent time to divide a plant. Dividing plants not only increases the stock of any clone but also prevents overcrowding. If a plant becomes too crowded, it tends to lose its older growths, which often shrivel and die prematurely. Once the vigor of a plant has been hampered by a situation such as this, it takes time for that plant to regain its former strength. Recovery may take several years, so it is best to prevent

Decay of potting medium may cause roots to rot and a plant's health to decline. If this cattleya is not repotted as soon as its developing growth initiates new roots, it may lose its root system because of the decaying medium.

this by dividing frequently. A division of a cattleya consisting of three or four pseudobulbs will flower on schedule the next season, whereas smaller divisions, like backbulb divisions, may require two or more years to regain flowering size.

Overpotting Another hazard, according to some individuals, is overpotting. Basically, if a cattleya or other sympodial plant is repotted in a container that will hold more than two years' new growth, it is overpotted. Overpotting in itself is not necessarily detrimental to the plant's growth, but it does use excessive amounts of potting medium, and the pot may — and usually does — take up much more bench space than the plant requires.

Having a variety of pot sizes, especially a few larger ones versus a lot of small ones, can cause problems with watering and fertilizing, so it is best to try to keep divisions small and variations in pot size to a minimum. In the case of monopodials, the pot should be large enough to sup-

Because of its elongate rhizome, *Bulbophyllum careyanum* is probably better suited for slab culture. Like some other "botanical" orchids, it can be attached to a piece of tree fern, cork or even a tree limb where it will last for years, needing remounting only when the support breaks down.

Overpotting orchids, like the cattleya here, can lead to overwatering because excess medium around the roots retains too much water. Match the size of the container to the plant's rootball, not the plant. If a cattleya is repotted in a container that will hold more than two years' new growth, it is overpotted.

port the plant. If a vanda falls over every time there is a slight breeze, then it needs a larger pot or should be cut back.

When repotting sympodials, it is important to remember that the rhizome should be parallel to the top surface of the medium, not with the back end down and the front end pointing up. Placing the rhizome even slightly below the surface of the potting mixture can be detrimental because it is easier for rot organisms to attack it, especially at the point where the young shoot buds are emerging. Also, if the front is raised above the medium, as the new roots emerge from the base of the pseudobulb and grow toward the medium, they are exposed for a longer period of time. Before they can enter the medium, they may be damaged or become easy prey for roaches and snails. Having the rhizome touching the medium allows

these new roots to penetrate the medium as soon as they emerge. Thus, they can begin their function of absorbing nutrients and water from the medium.

Repot at least once every two years. If sympodial plants are allowed to overgrow the pot, the new roots formed are usually long, stiff and brittle, and are difficult to handle when repotting. A plant with an extensive root system outside the pot often has many of these roots damaged when it is repotted. If the damage is extensive, the plants may even show signs of shriveling. Avoid this situation by repotting on schedule.

Even though it is a good idea to repot orchids every two years, there are some notable exceptions. Many of the so-called "botanicals" (usually tiny plants with tinier flowers) grow well on tree-fern plaques, cork bark and even tree limbs, and they often can be left for years and only remounted when the tree fern or cork bark breaks down. In fact, these plants often are most attractive when they form large masses and are better adapted to longtime undivided culture rather than the more rapid division carried out with cattleya clones.

Weeds

There are few orchid growers who have not, at one time or another, gone through a frustrating experience when their greenhouse was invaded by weeds, especially *Oxalis corniculata*. This pesky little plant has exploding seed capsules that fire their shiny black seeds all over the place. The seeds become attached wherever they strike — leaves, flowers, even walls. Eventually, the seeds are freed and fall to the ground or into the pots, where they germinate. Ferns can become weedy pests at times, too. Depending on the location and what other plants are grown with orchids, other weeds occasionally may become pests.

Although there are numerous herbicides on the market (both pre- and post-emergence types), none has been cleared for use on orchids. For this reason, the use of herbicides on orchid plants is clearly done at risk.

Three materials — Monuron (Karmex W or Telvar), Diuron (Karmex DW) and Princep-80W (Simazine-80W) — have been tried with success on some orchids. If it is decided to experiment with one of these materials, directions should be followed carefully. Make sure the plants are watered adequately a few hours prior to applying the herbicide because they should not be watered for several days after applying a herbicide in order to give the chemical adequate time to work. Herbicides may work on some orchids, but no one has tested any of these chemicals on all orchid genera and species. Consequently, if an orchid house that contains a wide variety of genera and species is sprayed experimentally, some plants may not tolerate the chemical and may lose their leaves or even be killed.

Weeds can be a problem, such as this oxalis growing at the base of this orchid.

Chemical Toxicity

Occasionally, orchid plants will be injured by a pesticide or herbicide spray or even by other chemical fumes or when plants come into contact with structures treated with certain wood and metal preservatives. The type of injury that occurs will vary, depending on the chemical and the physiological age and condition of the plant. Damage is usually the result of:
- Improper measurement of the chemical when mixing.
- Using the wrong chemical.
- Using the chemical at the wrong temperature Herbicide injury can include one or more of the following:
- Complete loss of foliage.
- Distortion of new growth.
- Loss of chlorophyll in all or parts of the leaves.
- Burning of the leaf margins.

Unfortunately, by the time most chemical injury is observed, there is little that can be done about it. Once a deformed

17

new growth is evident, the damage has occurred. It can be hoped that if the injury is not too severe, the plant will grow out of it. However, if the error is discovered at the time it occurs, immediately apply copious amounts of water to the medium and wash off the foliage. This will help reduce damage and may even prevent it from occurring. It is also wise to repot into a new medium to avoid any delayed reaction from materials that still may be lodged in the mix.

The wisest move is to use only those chemicals recommended for orchids and to follow the directions on the label explicitly.

There is also the possibility of damage arising from the misuse of pesticides, both fungicides and insecticides. The damage will vary from pesticide to pesticide and between and among plants. In general, the results of pesticide damage can be symptoms such as scorched leaves, dead spots on the leaves, bands of white or yellow on new leaves or even color change in the leaves.

Damage usually results from misuse of most pesticides. Errors in calculating the amount to use, applying pesticides too often (trying to use up the tank by going over the plants again) or spraying at too high (or low) a temperature all can lead to injury. Again, use only those pesticides labeled for orchids and follow the directions on the label.

Remember, too, that many pesticides can be harmful to humans as well as insects. Therefore, it is of utmost importance to realize this and take all necessary precautions to ensure the health and safety of the applicator and anyone in or near the greenhouse. It is wise to use a respirator and to wear protective clothing when spraying and to put signs on greenhouse doors warning that spraying has been done. Leave the signs posted until it is safe to reenter the greenhouse. It is also wise for persons who spray frequently to

When constructing a greenhouse or developing any growing area, select the proper building materials to safeguard the future health of the plants and people. Orchid plants can sustain injury when exposed to the fumes of, or by coming into contact with, certain wood and metal preservatives.

have a blood test every few months to be aware of their colonesterase levels. Not all chemicals have been tested on all orchid species and hybrids. Consequently, even though everything is done right, there may be some plants that are injured. If this occurs after two applications and the proper precautions have been taken, then try another recommended chemical to control the problem and see if the injured plants fare better.

Building Materials Orchid plants also can sustain injury when exposed to the fumes of, or by coming into contact with, certain wood and metal preservatives. Never paint greenhouse pipes with rust preservatives that contain tar oil. The fumes emanating from the pipes during winter, when the heat is on and the vents are closed, may injure all orchid types.

Avoid using creosote-treated wood in and around a greenhouse. The fumes are toxic and are impossible to seal in the wood by painting because the creosote will "bleed" through. Again, most of the damage will occur in the winter when the greenhouse is closed and there is little or no exchange of air with the outside. Any creosoted boards or posts in the greenhouse should be removed. At the same time, remove any soil that may contain creosote that bled from the posts.

For erecting a wooden greenhouse, select redwood or one of the other durable woods. When opting to use a cheaper grade of pine, do not use any that has been treated with penta (pentachlorophenal) because it, too, is toxic. There are other types of wood treated with preservatives that have been used successfully in greenhouse construction. Availability varies with locality, so it is best to check with local building-supply houses to see what is available.

No matter what type of material is used, use a good grade of white greenhouse paint. Painting serves three purposes:

■ It adds life to the greenhouse structure (painting retards weathering of wood).
■ It makes the greenhouse brighter.
■ It makes the surfaces easier to clean.

Some of today's paints seem to be relatively resistant to mildew and mold, thus are less apt to have those problems.

Air Pollution

Today the problems of air pollution and its increasing concentration and spread are becoming more and more evident. Fortunately, many orchid flowers appear to be almost resistant to the more common air pollutants (sulfur dioxide and ozone), so good flowering may occur even in areas of high pollution. However, there is one serious problem: the amount of ethylene in the air. Cattleya flowers that are just opening and young phalaenopsis buds are sensitive to ethylene in the air. Injury usually occurs in autumn and winter during periods of calm, cloudy weather when industrial and other fumes accumulate under the clouds. Although the gas rarely builds up to concentrations that could damage the plants, it often attains levels than can damage flowers and could be a threat to commercial growers.

As with most chemical damage, the degree of ethylene damage will be directly related to the concentration in the air and the length of time that the plants are exposed to it. O. Wesley Davidson showed that dry sepal (the drying of the tips of the sepals) was caused by 2 ppb (parts per billion) of ethylene in the atmosphere. The dorsal sepal shows the symptoms first. The tips are dry, papery and usually start discoloring a few days later. As the ethylene concentration increases, the amount of damage increases. When concentrations reach 40 to 50 ppb, both opening flowers and flowers that have just opened will collapse, and even the ovary will discolor, turning pinkish to cream, depending on the flower color.

In the case of phalaenopsis, it is the young flower buds that are most sensitive. Depending on the parentage of the plants, buds anywhere from $1/4$ to $3/4$ inches (6 to 18 mm) may be damaged by exposure to ethylene. The buds will turn a dirty creamy white about a day to a day and a half after exposure. Bud growth ceases, and in a week to 10 days, the discolored buds drop off, leaving the younger buds and open flowers on the stem. In cases where ethylene levels go as high as 75 ppb, even the newly opened phalaenopsis flowers may be injured. These blooms usually collapse a day after exposure, become papery a few days later, and eventually drop.

During the winter, there are occasions when, due to faulty flues or high concentrations of automobile fumes in foggy and overcast weather, ethylene may build up in the greenhouse to fairly high concentrations. If these concentrations are maintained for several days, then in addition to the flower damage, older leaves on cattleyas may turn yellow and eventually drop. The newer growths remain green. Occasionally, a faulty heater in a greenhouse can produce enough ethylene to cause cattleya leaves to yellow and fall prematurely. Constant checking of flues and pipes and the use of heaters that take air from outside the greenhouse for combustion and discharge combusted air outside the greenhouse will greatly reduce the chance of ethylene buildup from faulty furnaces.

Inspecting orchids frequently is recommended to detect the presence of pests, such as the mealybugs on these *Schombocattleya* flowers.

In areas where ethylene in the air is a problem, greenhouse air can be circulated through "scrubbers" that remove most of the ethylene, especially if the greenhouse is closed tightly. If air being introduced into the greenhouse from outside is passed through scrubbers, the greenhouse air will be virtually free of ethylene.

Miscellaneous Problems

Flowers In a variety of orchids, some abnormalities can be observed in flowers when the pollinia have been removed or the flower has been pollinated. Flowers of *Vanda* Miss Joaquim often are packaged in plastic bags for shipment to distant markets. If the bags are airtight and the pollinia of one or more flowers have been removed, the flowers will fade within 24 to 48 hours, turning to a dirty white. In *Cymbidium*, the lips and columns often turn an abnormal reddish color. There are reports by Oakes Ames of *Encyclia tampensis* (syn. *Epidendrum tampense*) doing the same thing. However, in some phalaenopsis, the petals thicken and turn green after pollination.

There have been more reports of abnormalities occurring in *Cymbidium* than in any other orchid genus. These flowers, which are normally long-lived, seem to age much more rapidly and show vivid color changes even when only the anther cap is removed.

Mice Mice can be a problem in a greenhouse, often eating flower buds or nectaries of such orchids as *Angraecum*. There are materials available to rid greenhouses of mice.

Cattleyas There are two distinct growth cycles in cattleyas, with one flowering while the bud sheaths are green and the other flowering when the sheaths are brown and dry. Occasionally, a situation arises that resembles the latter type of sheath development but is destructive. There are times when the sheaths turn yellow then dark brown and become soft and mushy. If these sheaths are allowed to remain on the plants, the flower buds inside will rot. If the sheaths are removed as soon as they start to turn brown, the buds usually can be saved and will develop into normal flowers. It is essential to be able to separate the normal light brown and drying sheaths, as in *Cattleya trianaei* from those that turn dark brown. Unfortunately, the cause of this malady is unknown. It seems to be confined mainly to *Cattleya* and allied genera.

Pseudobulbs Occasionally, a pseudobulb will have one or more cracks, usually horizontally. Some cracks are deep and pseudobulbs have been known to snap off

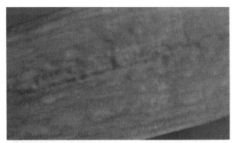

Cattleya leaf showing severe early stage of mesophyll cell collapse.

Phalaenopsis leaves showing the typical corky bumps following oedema injury.

at the crack due to the weight of the flowers. This cracking is not widespread and is limited to a small variety of plants. It appears that it is probably a genetic condition, because there does not seem to be any nutritional or other cultural condition that has any effect on its frequency or severity. Longitudinal cracks occur in some pseudobulbs, but are usually of little significance.

Ants *Myrmechophila* (syn. *Schomburgkia), Catasetum* and several other genera of orchids that have large, frequently hollow pseudobulbs are often homes for colonies of ants. Trying to remove one of these plants from a tree in its native habitat may result in an unpleasant encounter with an angry horde of these insects. If there is a large number of ants around a schomburgkia in the greenhouse, then chances are they are setting up housekeeping in the pseudobulbs. Normal ant sprays quickly eliminate the problem.

Mesophyll Cell Collapse Frequently during spring months orchid plants, especially phalaenopsis, exhibit symptoms that look like virus. In reality, this is a situation known as mesophyll cell collapse. It is most evident in early spring, and symptoms are usually observed about six weeks after damage has occurred. The damage is the result of mesophyll cells collapsing after exposure to low temperatures. The first signs are usually yellow, slightly depressed streaks on developing leaves. The streaks become more pronounced and turn tan in color. Eventually, black pitting develops along the streak.

The most sensitive leaves are newly expanding and usually less than three-fourths mature. Leaves of this age will show signs of collapse after two hours at 45 F (8 C). At lower temperatures, the symptoms are more severe with less exposure. However, a phalaenopsis with all mature leaves can withstand eight hours at 35 F (2 C) without any problems.

Oedema This physiological disorder that occurs occasionally on orchid plants is more cosmetic than harmful. It appears as small watery blisters, usually on the underside of the leaf, but can occur on both leaf surfaces. In severe cases, the blisters may rupture. Over time, the blisters will heal as cork-covered bumps and remain as long as the leaf is attached to the plant. Oedema occurs under certain climatic conditions wherein the roots of the plant take up moisture faster than it is lost by the leaves through evapotranspiration. This excess moisture causes the cells in soft tissue to swell and form external blisters. Aside from unsightly leaves, no real harm is done to the plant. Even in severe cases, where the underside of the leaf is completely peppered with small blisters, the leaves remain on the plant. It is more apt to occur in the spring or autumn.

Biological Control of Insects and Mites

By James F. Price, PhD

RECENTLY THERE HAS BEEN AN increased emphasis on controlling insects and mites naturally, without the application of toxic chemicals. Before, meager supportive scientific data specific for diverse crops, high per-acre-values and associated risks, and the tradition of effective pesticides played roles in restricting the use of biological controls in floriculture. But today, the more inclusive integrated pest management (IPM), sometimes with its biological control component, has become accepted as a standard practice among leaders in the floricultural industry.

Successful application of biological control in orchid collections can be a reality in simple pest environments where only one or a few arthropod pests effect losses, and where general biological control techniques for those pests have been developed. Individual orchid growers, guided by experienced state Cooperative Extension Service personnel and commercial biological-control personnel, could begin to integrate biological controls into their existing IPM programs.

Elements of Integrated Pest Management

A critical aspect of initiating first ventures in biological control in orchids is to possess experience in practicing effective IPM, including:

- Obtaining stock free of pests.
- Practicing effective crop sanitation.
- Excluding pests from production areas.
- Knowing and scouting for pests regulary and maintaining records of pest incidence.
- Applying least ecologically disruptive pesticides based only on their need as indicated by scouting.
- Practicing sound crop culture in all phases of production.

Orchid growers who have not fully applied the principles of IPM should not attempt the more complicated biological-control component of IPM until having gained experience in general aspects.

Hobbyists should not expect to establish biological control of two or more pests immediately; rather they initially should identify one pest for this technique. With experience, biological controls may be applied to additional pests. General systems of biological control of four groups of orchid pests are well developed and could be practical for IPM programs in orchids: fungus gnats, mealybugs, aphids (but probably not the melon aphid) and spider mites.

As in many new ventures, persistence is required in order to be successful in establishing biological control. Gardeners who grow orchids for the first time should expect success, but also should be prepared for failure. So it is with orchid growers attempting biological control for the first time — they should expect success, but should be prepared for failure. Just as experience transforms gardeners into successful orchid growers, experience can transform orchid growers into successful practitioners of biological control.

For biological control to flourish, cultural practices must be examined for compatibility with the new system of control and must be adjusted accordingly. For instance, some commonly used pesticides are detrimental to or even incompatible with certain biological control agents. Residues from pyrethroid pesticides can remain lethal to the *Phytoseiulus persimilis*, predator of spider mites, for two months or more. Disruptive pesticides and their residues must be eliminated or restricted.

Suppliers of biological-control agents can provide the information known on effects of pesticides and other elements of orchid culture on their beneficials.

Little research has been performed specifically to evaluate biological-control methods for insect and mite pests of orchids. At this time, orchid growers must borrow from experiences gained from other situations and refine the methods themselves. The host crop can make a difference in the performance of a biological-control agent, so bridging techniques from one situation to orchids must not be considered certain. Always experiment with a few orchids before treating an entire collection.

This chapter has been developed from literature concerning biological control in numerous horticultural crops and from experiences of the author and his colleagues. The following information should be used only as a general guide in developing the biological-control component of IPM on orchids.

The biological-control agents discussed here are ecologically specialized and cannot feed on orchids, even when hungry. Most will starve once they cannot find sufficient pest prey.

Control of Fungus Gnats
Hypoaspis miles

This fungus gnat predator is a brown mite that lives on the soil surface. Commercial insectaries produce *Hypoaspis miles* mites for sale mixed with a moist, peat carrier in 1 quart containers sufficient to treat 500 to 1,000 pots. Spoon the recommended amount of mites and carrier onto the soil surface where the mite will thrive on fungus gnat larvae and other tiny insects. Apply this predatory mite to the orchids before fungus gnats begin to build up significantly. One application may be sufficient for control in about three to five weeks.

Steinernema feltiae

When fungus gnat populations are already built up, one or two applications of the predatory nematode, *Steinernema feltiae*, three to four weeks apart, may be useful. The nematodes are shipped ready to be mixed with water and poured onto the soil as a drench. The nematode attacks the larval fungus gnat in the soil, releasing a bacterium inside the fungus gnat resulting in its death. The nematode can reproduce in the dead larva to kill more fungus gnats later. *Steinernema feltiae* nematode and *H. miles* mite can be used together.

Control of Mealybugs
Mealybug Destroyer [*Cryptolaemus montrouzieri*]

This black/dark brown and orange lady beetle is effective at controlling high densities of mealybugs. Both the adults and the larvae (which look similar to mealybugs) are predaceous on several mealybug species. Release two to five adults per infested plant. Because lady beetles tend to fly away when food is scarce, it may be useful to screen the greenhouse vents to prevent escape. This beneficial insect is ineffective during the cold, short days of winter.

Control of Aphids
Aphid Midge [*Aphidoletes aphidimyza*]

This predator of aphids, which is shipped as pupae in bottles, can effectively control moderately high aphid densities. Sometimes the aphid midge has advanced to the adult stage before the user receives the shipment. Sprinkle the pupae (or adults) and the vermiculite carrier shipped with the predators onto protected surfaces near infested plants. Two to four weekly applications of one to six pupae per plant may be required. As the mosquito like adults emerge, they search for aphid colonies in which to lay their eggs. Larvae hatch from the eggs in a few days and begin to feed on and kill aphids. Larvae may be recognized as orange or pink maggots among the aphids. This predator can reproduce in the greenhouse to control aphids throughout the season, however it requires access to soil, sawdust or peat under production benches to pupate. Night lighting may be required under short-day conditions to keep this predator active.

The aphid midge efficiently attacks many species of aphids, but is inefficient in controlling the common melon aphid. For success with this species, large numbers of aphid midge predators must be released.

Aphidius matricariae

This is an effective parasite of the green peach aphid and others, not including the melon aphid. It is a tiny wasp that does not sting people. Release adult wasps at low aphid densities at about three wasps for every 10 plants each week for at least three weeks. This parasite is not affected by short-day conditions, but may not be effective in the spring and summer when aphids reproduce rapidly and parasites of this parasite ("hyperparasites") are particularly active. Aphids killed by this wasp turn brown and swell, resulting in an appearance characteristic of a paper sack. A new generation of adult wasps cuts round holes in the tops of dead aphids and emerges to seek other aphids to parasitize.

Yellow sticky traps, used to monitor thrips, fungus gnats, aphids, etc., also attract A. matricariae and can reduce the parasite's effectiveness. Do not use them in the vicinity where A. matricariae is released. Blue sticky traps are not detrimental.

Control of Spider Mites
Phytoseiulus persimilis

This predatory mite is the most widely used biological-control agent in horticul-

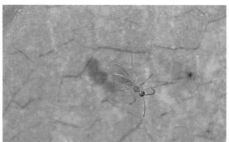

An adult predatory midge, Aphidoletes aphidimyza. Adult aphid midges lay eggs near aphid colonies. The eggs hatch into larvae that feed on the aphids.

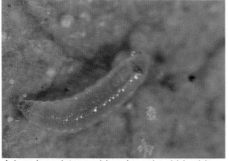

A larval predatory midge. Larval aphid midges kill many species of aphids by biting the aphid at a leg joint and sucking its fluids.

Aphids parasitized by Aphidius matricariae die and acquire the swollen and brown appearance of a paper sack. Here, an Aphidius matricariae adult emerges from a parasitized aphid. After the parasite has killed the aphid, developed and emerged, the adult searches for other aphids in which to lay eggs and repeat the parasitization process.

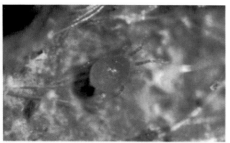

An adult *Phytoseiulus persimilis* predatory mite. *Phytoseiulus persimilis* predators feed only on spider mites and cannot harm plants.

ture. It is shipped usually in plastic bottles containing about 2,000 mites mixed with a dry vermiculite carrier. The orange, fast-moving predators should be applied as soon as spider mites become evident and at an average of one predator per orchid plant. Sprinkle the predatory mites onto leaves or onto pot surfaces. Spider mite colonies should be monitored twice weekly and predators released again in two weeks if many colonies are found to be without predators. *Phytoseiulus persimilis* seems to be more effective on short, compact plants than on tall, open ones.

This predator reproduces quickly and can consume most available prey. Therefore, the population can die of starvation within several weeks. Monitor the crop and release new predators when spider mites appear.

Control of Other Pests

Possibilities exist for biological control of additional pests, including species of scales, thrips and caterpillars. Biological control methods for these pests are less developed and should be considered only by growers with considerable experience with biological control.

Obtaining Biological Control Agents

Several insectaries in North America, Europe and elsewhere produce one or more of the biological-control agents useful in orchid protection. Many more busi-

nesses obtain the agents from producers and then resell them. Availability of various biological-control agents was summarized by W.T. Thompson in *A Worldwide Guide to Beneficial Animals Used for Pest Control Purposes* (Thimson Publications, Fresno, California. 1992) www.agbook.com/worldwideguide.asp and by C.D. Hunter in *Suppliers of Beneficial Organisms in North America* (California EPA, Department of Pesticide Regulation, 1020 N. Street, Room 161, Sacramento, California 95814. 1994. www.cdpr.ca.gov/docs/ipminov/bersuppl.htm.) These volumes also serve as an excellent resource to obtain biological control agents.

In selecting a provider of biological-control agents, an orchid grower should ascertain that the provider deals only in high quality, healthy organisms, produced by a reputable firm, and shipped fresh to the user. The provider should be knowledgeable on the agents sold and alternatives to them and should provide ample support information.

IPM programs in orchids that include biological components can be at least as effective and cost efficient as are programs founded solely on pesticides.

To learn more about natural control of pests, consult *Knowing and Recognizing the Biology of Glasshouse Pests and Their Natural Enemies*, by M. Malais and W. J. Ravensberg (Koppert B. V., Berkel en Rodenrijs, The Netherlands. 1992. www.koppertonline.com/showitem.asp?vis=home&item=product&id=126.) Available from organizations in the United States, including G.J. Ball, Inc., West Chicago, Illinois) and the second edition of *Biological Pest Management for Interior Plantscapes*, by M.Y. Steiner and D.P. Elliott (AECV87-E1. Alberta Environmental Centre, Vegreville, Alberta. 1992).

Pesticides: Selection, Application and Storage

By Gary W. Simone, PhD, and Donald E. Short, PhD

PESTICIDES REPRESENT A MAJOR component of an integrated crop-management strategy directed toward successful orchid production. When a pesticide is targeted for use, this action should trigger a reassessment of such production parameters as relative humidity, temperature, fertilization, timing and duration of irrigation, general sanitation, etc., that may strongly influence the degree of performance achieved by the product's use. Pesticides, when used correctly, can provide great benefits to orchid production. When used carelessly, however, these same products can cause varying degrees of plant damage — including plant death.

The success of controlling insects and diseases of orchids often revolves around the understanding and application of a few basic rules. In the use and application of pesticides, several basics became major concerns. These can be referred to as the five Rs:

■ The right identification of the disease, insect or mite involved.

■ The right pesticide for the target pest or disease.

■ The right dosage of the correct pesticide.

■ The right application site and method for this pesticide.

■ The right timing for the pesticide application.

What is the right identification of the problem? Due to the broad array of organisms that may be involved with inciting damage to orchids, it is often a monumental task to be familiar with all of them. In addition, the identification of many plant pathogens, mites and insects requires equipment and expertise not often available to the orchid grower. Thus, the most reliable source of these identifications is the diagnostic laboratory. Every state has a "land grant" university in which many agricultural sciences are represented. These academic departments (like Entomology or Plant Pathology) cooperate with the Federal Cooperative Extension Service to support specific individuals and/or facilities to assist state residents with plant-related problems. Consult the County Cooperative Extension Service to access the diagnostic facility in your state as well as for proper instructions on the collection and submission of plant samples for diagnosis.

In strongly agricultural states, similar diagnostic facilities may be available within the State Department of Agriculture; for example, as in California, Florida and Pennsylvania. Additionally, there may be privately run diagnostic laboratories with qualified personnel to assist with problem diagnosis. There is also the value of experience that is accrued by growers during the production of orchids. The use of available printed material, photographs of known problems, and production records can often clue a grower into the correct identity of an insect or disease problem. The benefit in obtaining an accurate diagnosis is in the implementation of the correct control measures (including pesticides) with no loss in time or damage sustained from incorrect product use.

Choosing a Pesticide

Many sources of information exist to determine the right pesticide. Each state cooperative extension service maintains up-to-date leaflets, fact sheets, circulars and other publications with recommendations on specific pests. Dealers and suppliers of pesticides have written information available. Trade journals can offer valuable assistance. Other orchid enthusiasts can also offer advice. No matter what source of pesticide information is consulted, remember that the legality of a product's use rests with the label text. Read the label to confirm that a product can be legally, effectively and safely used on orchids.

Determining the Amount The pesticide label is the ultimate source of informa-tion including the correct amount of pesticide to use. Read and reread the label directions on the container carefully and follow them explicitly. Too little pesticide may not control the pest. In addition, many of the newer, systemic pesticides have narrow modes of action such that a dosage reduction can encourage the development of chemical tolerance in an insect, mite or fungus population. The use of too much product may exceed the limit of plant safety and result in plant damage (phytotoxicity). Remember that each pesticide product has a rate designed to ensure the persistence of an effective dosage for that pest or pathogen for the length of the application interval. Reducing the rate can make the orchid plant vulnerable to additional disease or injury prior to the next scheduled pesticide application. Never rely on any source other than the labels for dosage information.

Application Sites and Methods The federal legislation that defines pesticide use is called the Federal Insecticide, Fungicide, and Rodenticide Act (FIFRA), originally passed in 1947. This law and its more recent amendments indicate that there are prescribed "sites" for pesticide use that must appear on the label for legal use of the product. The most relevant sites to orchid production include the "field" (landscape, outdoors), "greenhouse" and the "interiorscape" (interior landscape, indoors). Present interpretation of this part of FIFRA in most states is that it is illegal to use any pesticide in an aforementioned site when the label text does not reflect that site word or equivalent descriptor.

The right application method can mean

Pesticide Laws

According to the Federal Insecticide, Fungicide, and Rodenticide Act all pesticides must be handled and applied in strict accordance with directions on the pesticide-container label. Also, if a pesticide is used in the greenhouse or interiorscape, it must be labeled for such use.

The Act includes a section that states that it is a violation to use a registered pesticide in a manner not permitted by the labeling with the exception of four specific areas. Under Section FIFRA 2(ee) it is not misuse to:

■ Apply a pesticide at any dosage, concentration or frequency less than that specified on the labeling. But lowering rates may lead to tolerance in the target pest or pathogen population.

■ Apply a pesticide against any pest not specified on the labeling if the application is to the crop, animal or site specified on the labeling (unless the label states that the pesticide may be used only against pests specified on the label).

■ Employ any method of application not prohibited by the labeling. The exception is chemigation. No equipment can change the dose per volume of diluent ratio on the label.

■ Mix a pesticide or pesticides with a fertilizer when such mixture is not prohibited by the labeling.

---

several things. Pesticides can be applied as foliar sprays, root drenches, plant/cutting dips or as media-incorporated treatments. These methods must be stated on the label for legal product use. Foliar application of pesticides requires thorough coverage of the leaves (especially the undersides), stems and pseudobulbs. Spray to the point of runoff. Remember to use hollow or solid-cone nozzle tips for the application of fungicides and insecticides (not flat fan-nozzle tips).

Some pesticides break down (hydrolyze) in the spray tank when mixed with water above pH 7. Growers should be aware of their water pH and when above 7, a buffering solution should be added to maintain pH in the 6.5 to 7 range. Many growers prefer to use a spreader sticker to aid in pesticide adherence to the plants, especially when wettable powders are used.

Read the label to ensure the plant safety of this practice with each product. Drench fungicides must be uniformly delivered through the root zone to be effective. Additionally, the right application method also reflects equipment. Pesticide-application equipment is quite diverse and includes such sprayers as: simple trombone-action, compressed air, 3- to 5- gallon knapsack; roller, centrifugal or piston pumps; air blast, foggers and chemigation systems. Any spray equipment can be used if the equipment is stated on the label and the equipment use is not prohibited by the label.

Remember the following two qualifications when choosing spray equipment. The use of chemigation must be present on the label for legal use with any product. The choice of a specific piece of spray equipment not prohibited by the label; for example, a fogger, cannot violate the rate information on the label. For example, a pesticide label rate of one-half pound per 100 gallons of water cannot be legally used in a fogger at the one-half-pound in 5 gallons of water.

Timing Inspect plants twice per week for any evidence of insects or diseases. Infestations are much more easily controlled in the initial stages. Be sure to fol-

Poison Control Centers

Poison information centers are located throughout the United States and are on call 24 hours a day. In an emergency, call the center closest to you, but it is preferable to let your doctor consult the center. The National Pesticide Information Center (Oregon State University), which is open seven days a week, 6:30 am–4:30 pm, will refer you to the appropriate poison control center (telephone 1-800-858-7378; e-mail npic@ace.orst.edu; Web site npic.orst.edu).

low container-label directions regarding correct interval for follow-up applications and any possible adverse interactions with temperature extremes. FIFRA amendment Section 2(ee) in 1981 allows for longer spray intervals than appear on the label but not shorter ones.

Schedule foliar applications after the foliage has dried from irrigation to maximize the drying and/or absorption time into the plant for the pesticide. Similarly, schedule drench applications for the maximum period of media-pesticide exposure prior to the next irrigation. Never drench stressed plants.

Toxicity of Pesticides

A question frequently asked concerning the use of pesticides is, "How toxic is the pesticide to humans?" The standards used to compare toxicities are based on tests with small laboratory animals. The toxicity of a pesticide is based upon the LD_{50} (lethal dose required to kill 50 percent of the test population) of the pesticide formulation relating to oral, dermal and inhalation exposure. The required signal (warning) words mandatory on all labels concerning the toxicity of the pesticide

Toxicity of Pesticides for Orchids[1]

Pesticide Name		Usage	Toxicity	Acute	Inhalation
Generic[2]	Trade Site	Class	Oral LD50 (mg/kg)	Dermal LD50 (mg/kg)	MG/I
abamectin	Avid 0.15EC	F, G,	II	>1800	
acephate	Acephate Pro 75, WSP	G	III	>10,250	>14.8
	Adress T/O				
	Sedagi Acephate 75 SP				
	1300 Orthene TR				
	Ornimental Spray 75, 97				
azadirachtin	Ornazin 3% EC	F, G	II	>2000	
	Azatin XL				
azinphos-methyl	Guthion Solupak	F	I	88-222	
bacillus thuringiensis					
israelensis	Gnathol	F, G	IV	>2,000	
beauveria bassiana	Botanigard 22 WP	F, G	IV		
	Bontanigard ES	F, G			
	Naturalis L	F, G			
bifenazate	Floramite	F, G		>2,000	>4.4
	Floramite SC	F, G			
bifenthrin	Attain TR	G	II	>2,000	
	Talstar GH Prescription				
	Talstar Flowable				
	Talstar N	F, G			
	Talstar Nursery Flowable	F, G			
	Talstar Nursery				
	Granular				
carbaryl	Sevin SL	F	II,III	>2,000	
chloefenapyr	Pylon	G	III	>2,000	1.9
clarified hydrophobic	Triact 70	F, G			
clofentezine	Ovation SC	F, G	III	>2100	
cyfluthrin	Decathlon 20 WP	F, G			
cyromazine	Citation	F, G	III	>3,100	
deltamethrin	Deltagard GC 5 SC	F	II	>2,000	2.69
diazinon	KnoxOut NL	F		>2,020	5.4
	Diazinon 50W				
	Diazinon AG 500 (Micro Flo)				
difubenzuron	Adept	F, G	III	>10,000	
dimethoate	Dimethoate 400	F	II	>400	
disulfoton	Di-Syston 15%G	F	I		
endosulfan	Endosulfan 50WP	F, G	I	>500	
	Phaser 50WSB, 3EC	F, G			
	Thiodan 3 EC				
etoxazole	Tetrasan 5 WDG	F, G		>2,000	1.09
fenbutatin-oxide	Vendex 50WP	F, G	I, III	>2,000	
fenoxycarb	Precision	F, G	IV	>2,000	
	Preclude TR	G			
fenpropathrin	Tame	F, G	II	>2,000	
fenpyroximate	Akari 5SC	G			
hexythiazox	Hexygon DF	F	IV	>5,000	>2.0
	Hexygon	F			
imidacloprid	Marathon 1% Granular	F, G			
	Marathon 60 WP	F, G			
	Marathon II	F, G			
iron phosphate	Monterey Sluggo-Ag	F, G			
lambda-cyhalothrin	Scimitar SC	F, G	I	632	

Toxicity of Pesticides for Orchids[1]

Pesticide Name Generic[2]	Trade Site	Usage Class	Toxicity Oral LD50 (mg/kg)	Acute Dermal LD50 (mg/kg)	Inhalation MG/I
malathion	Atrapa 5E	F	III	>2,000	>5.2
	Gowan Malathion 8F				
	Malathion 5EC				
	Prozap 57EC				
metaldehyde	Deadline Bullets, M-PS	F, G	III		
	Durham Metaldehyde				
	G 3.5, 7.5	G			
	Trails End 3.5, LG				
	Prozap Snail & Slug Ag	F. G			
methidathion	Supracide 25-W	F	I, III	1546	3.6
methiocarb	Mesurol 75-W	F, G	II, III		
naled	Dibrom 8 E	G	I	1100	
novaluron	Pedestal	F, G	I, V	>2000	>5.15
oxydemeton-methyl	Metasystox-R	F	II	1350	
permethrin	Astro	F, G	II, III	>2,500	
potassium salts			II, IV		
of fatty acids	Inscticidal Soap 49.52 CE	F, G			
	M-Pede	F, G			
propargite	Ornamite	F	I	>4,000	
pymetrozine	Endeavor	F, G	III	>2,000	>3.09
pyrethrins and			III	>1,800	
piperonly butoxide	1100 Pyrethrun	G			
	Pyreth-It	f, G			
	Pyrenone Crop spray				
pyrethrins, piperonyl butoxide and silicon dioxide	Diatect Multipurpose Insecticide II	F			
pyrethrins, rotenone and other cube resins	Pyrellin EC	F, G			
pyridaben	Sanmite 75W	F, G	III	>2,000	0.62–0.66
pyriproxyfen	Distance	F, G	II	>2,000	>5.6
refined petroleum			III, IV		
distillate	Saf-T-Side Spray Oil	G			
	Ultra-ine Oil	F, G			
s-kinoprene	Enstar II	G	II	9,000	>200
spinosad	Conserve SC	F, G			
tau-fluvalinate	Mark Aquaflow	F, G	III	20,000	
steinernema Carpocapsae	Millenium	G, G			
steinernema feltiae	Nemasys	F, G			

[1]Data summarized from select publications and pesticide material safety data sheets. Products included or excluded do not constitute endorsements for use. Remember the product label is the ultimate expression of legal use.

[2]Generic products without trade names are legal uses in the Federal Register, but no available brands could be found listing orchids on the label.

[3]Usage site abbreviations are: F = field, G = greenhouse and I = interiorscape.

[4]Acute oral and dermal toxicity data followed by the letter 'a' were derived from studies involving rabbits rather than rats.

[5]Toxicology values based on technical grade material.

formulation and the toxicity of pesticides for orchids are listed in this chapter.

Dry Flowables (DF) are sprayable, solid pesticide formulations that represent improvements over wettable powders. Chief advantages are reduced dust during loading/mixing, better shipping qualities (no "packing") and improved solubility.

Dusts (D) are dry mixtures of insecticides with inert powders. The dusts are composed of fine particles, about 250 to 350 mesh. They are usually sold in strengths of 0.5 to 10 percent and are applied in the form purchased. Due to their small particle size, dusts will float in air and are easily blown away during application. They generally leave a good residue as long as they remain dry. But when they become moist, they may cake and become ineffective. However, a slight amount of moisture on a plant may actually aid in the distribution and adherence of the dust to the treated surface.

Emulsifiable Concentrates (EC) are formulations that contain the pesticide dissolved in an oil-based solvent. An emulsifier is added to enable the insecticide and oil to mix with water. Concentrates require little agitation in the spray tank, are nonabrasive and nonclogging to spray nozzles, adhere to foliage better and provide longer residual control than other formulations. They usually are more phytotoxic than wettable powder formulations, however.

Flowables (F) are the suspension of a solid in a liquid, not dissolved. Flowables are finely ground and added to a liquid along with wetting agents and diluents to form a suspension that can be mixed with water. They seldom clog, need only moderate agitation and handle like an EC.

Granules (G) commonly contain from one to 20 percent of the pesticide impregnated into highly absorptive materials like clays, with particles ranging in size from 30 to 60 mesh. Granules are heavier than wettable powders. This minimizes drift and prevents undue loss of pesticide and undesirable contamination of areas bordering those being treated. Granules are normally applied to potting mix rather than to foliage.

Miscible Concentrates (MC, ML) are liquid formulations where two or more liquids are capable of being mixed in various proportions and remaining mixed under normal environmental conditions.

Water Dispersible Granules (WDG) are a new pesticide formulation that offers advantages over wettable powders. The WDGs reduce hazards from dusts arising from WP formulations, do not "settle out" or "pack" in transit and are easier to measure. WDGs can be formulated to concentrate the active ingredients and offer cleanup advantages during pesticide spills.

Wettable Powders (WP) are formulated by adding a carrier plus a wetting agent to the pesticide. Powders are usually less phytotoxic and less odorous than concentrates. They tend to clog screens below the nozzle tips, require more agitation in the spray tank, are somewhat abrasive to nozzle tips and may leave a visible deposit on the foliage. Some growers add a green vegetable dye to the spray mixture to minimize this residue.

Compatibility of Pesticides

Many growers want to mix pesticides to control several pests in one application. This can be (and often is) done. However, spray-tank mixtures of insecticides, miticides or fungicides may result in phytotoxicity that does not occur from use of any one of the materials alone. Before pesticides are tank-mixed, consult a compatibility chart to determine if they are physically compatible. Compatibility charts are published annually and may be obtained from Meister Publishing Company, Willoughby, Ohio 44094 www.meistermedia.com

A general rule of thumb is to mix wettable powders with wettable powders, emulsifiable concentrates with emulsifiable concentrates, and mixes should be compounds of the same class and preferably the same brand if possible. Always read the container labels for any information regarding tank mixes.

It is inevitable that some desirable combinations of pesticides are not included in available, printed compatibility literature. In these situations, orchid growers can evaluate the physical and chemical compatibility of potential tank-mix combinations as well as their plant safety. A simple jar test for compatibility will enable growers to evaluate new pesticide mixtures. This test requires a series of clean mason jars or similar one-quart glass containers, the respective pesticides and a simple calculator to reduce pesticide rates to a one-pint-volume basis. Most house dictionaries have a "Weights and Measures" chart giving the equivalences between different volume measurements, such as teaspoons and fluid ounces, while weight-to-volume conversions for specific pesticides are often given on the label. Remember that every dry pesticide formulation has its unique density so there is no generic number of measuring spoons per ounce weight.

Steps to conduct this jar test:

Step 1   Fill each jar with 1 pint (473 ml) of clean water.

Step 2   Label one jar for each pesticide to be mixed and one jar for the composite mixture.

Step 3   If a surfactant is normally used, add this to each jar in the following ratio: [Liquid surfactant: For each 1 fluid ounce in the surfactant rate per 100 gallons, add 2 drops per 1 pint of water.]

Step 4   Calculate the correct rates per product on a pint basis.

Step 5   Add the single pesticides to their respective jars.

Step 6   Add the pesticide mixture to the jar in the following sequence: WP, then G, then DF, then WDG, then F and finally EC.

Step 7   Shake each jar vigorously for 30 seconds (with lid tightly sealed).

Step 8   Observe each jar for evidence of physical and/or chemical incompatibility after 30 seconds.

Step 9   Never reuse jars for food or feed purposes.

Physical incompatibility is expressed as the inability of two or more chemicals to mix — forming a layered or "puddled effect" like oil on water. Do not trust combinations with this appearance. Chemical incompatibility is expressed by the formation of a precipitate or flocculent material that settles rapidly to the bottom of the jar. This reaction indicates chemical interaction among pesticides that may mean loss of function or plant safety and certainly poses a strong likelihood of plugging nozzle screens and spray tips. These combinations also should be avoided.

Determining jar compatibility is the first part of a two-part safety evaluation for pesticide combinations. Part two is a small-scale spray or drench trial on a finite number of orchids. Select six to eight orchids of similar age and genus or species. Label half of the pots as "sprayed/(date)" and the other pots as "unsprayed/(date)." Apply the potential pesticide mixture to half the plants in a normal spray procedure (time of day, volume, equipment, etc.). Maintain these plants in the normal production area and observe them for acute symptoms of phytotoxicity (0.54 days) or chronic symptoms (period of weeks to months).

Pesticide phytotoxicity appears in several ways, but probably five types of damage most commonly occur.

Phytotoxicity commonly appears as a combination of two or more of these five symptoms:

Acute

■ Burn — this type of damage may appear on the tip or the margin; spots on the leaf or the entire leaf surface may appear burned. The growing tip or bud may also be killed.

■ Necrosis (or death of the plant tissue) —similar to burn and affecting plants in the same manner.

Chlorosis

■ Chlorosis (a yellowing or bleaching effect) — may appear as spots, tip yellowing or as a general chlorosis of the entire leaf.

■ Leaf Distortion — may appear as curling, crinkling or cupping of the leaf.

■ Stunting or abnormal growth.

Although any portion of the plant may be affected, the new growth is most likely to show damage when sprays are applied. When soil drenches are used, root tissue may be injured, causing stunting or slow plant decline. Soil drenches can damage the foliage, but the older leaves usually show damage rather than the new growth. The chronic development of plant injury through abnormal growth will likely occur on new growth.

The following are general rules or guidelines to help reduce phytotoxicity, and they should be observed by all growers when applying pesticides.

■ Do not apply a pesticide to plants that are stressed. Plants should be growing at their optimum.

■ Spray only to the point of runoff. Excessive volumes of any pesticide may cause phytotoxicity.

■ Avoid spraying under extremely hot, sunny conditions. Spray in the mornings when possible, preferably between 6 a.m. and 10 a.m. When air or plant tissue temperature is approximately 90 F (32 C) or higher, damage will likely occur. On bright sunny days, leaf-tissue temperatures may be 5 to 15 F (2.75 to 8.25 C) higher than the surrounding air, thus increasing the possibility of injury. Also, slow-growing plants are more likely to be damaged. Avoid temperature extremes, either high or low.

■ Do not apply pesticides under conditions that will not promote drying. Plants sprayed when cool, humid conditions exist for extended periods will remain wet for long periods of time and increase the probability of injury. This is one reason plants sprayed under greenhouse conditions are more likely to be damaged.

■ Never spray plants when they need water. Wilted or dry plants are extremely sensitive to spray injury.

Aerosols Almost all aerosol formulations of pesticides will cause phytotoxicity if applied at less than the recommended distance between aerosol nozzle and plant. The distance usually recommended is 18 to 20 inches (45 to 50 cm). In some experiments, it was found that almost all of 23 aerosols tested were phytotoxic when applied at 8 inches (20 cm), but only two of these caused severe injury at 12 to 16 inches (30 to 40 cm) from the plant. Most aerosols will damage plants when applied at temperatures above 85 F (29.5 C) and when the foliage is wet. Be sure to read the container label carefully before aerosols are used.

Study the label and any brochures (labeling) that are available concerning the particular pesticide to be used for dosage rates, application instructions, phytotoxicity information and other details. Do not overdose.

Pesticide and Application Safety

General Precautions Following these guidelines will reduce accidents before, during and after application of pesticides.

■ Read the label. This is the first rule of

safety in using any pesticide. Read the directions and precautions label and carefully follow all directions and precautions printed on it.

- Persons mixing or applying pesticides should wear protective clothing consisting of coveralls over long-sleeved shirt and long trousers; shoes, socks, chemical resistant gloves and either goggles plus a vapor respirator or a face shield, depending on the product label.
- When opening a container of liquid pesticide, keep your face away from the cap or lid.
- Mix or prepare dusts or sprays outdoors or in a well-ventilated room. Be especially careful when handling the concentrated pesticides.
- In handling any pesticide, avoid contact with the skin. Do not get the pesticide near your mouth, eyes or nose.
- If pesticide gets in your eyes, flush the eyes with water for five minutes; get medical attention.
- Never smoke, eat, or drink while handling a pesticide. After finishing the work, wash exposed skin surfaces with soap and water immediately.
- If you spill pesticide on clothing, launder the clothing before wearing it again.
- If you become ill during or shortly after using a pesticide, call a physi-cian immediately. From the container label, read to him or her the names of the active chemical ingredients; follow his or her instructions for first-aid treatment.
- Store pesticides in closed, well-labeled containers where children or pets cannot reach them. Do not store them under the sink, in the pantry, the medicine cabinet or near food of any kind.
- Store application equipment as you do pesticides — out of the reach of children or pets.

Pesticide users fall into either the private-use category (hobbyist) or the more regulated agricultural-use arena that will include commercial growers, as well as institutional orchid collections where employees are exposed to pesticide use. The laws governing worker exposure to pesticides have been revised so that product labels have revised text dealing with aspects of worker exposure to pesticides. For agricultural-use situations involving pesticides, worker re-entry rules now exist for all products used.

Written or oral warning must be given to workers who are expected to be in or about the treated area. When oral warnings are issued, they must be given in a language customarily understood by the workers. Oral warnings must be given if there exists a suspicion that written warnings cannot be understood by workers. Warnings must include the following information.

(Example Only):

"(CAUTION). OR (WARNING). OR (DANGER/POISON) Area treated with (product name) on (date of application). Do not enter without appropriate protective clothing until (re-entry period) has passed. In case of contact flush skin or eyes with plenty of water. For eyes, consult a physician if irritation persists."

The minimum re-entry period for pesticide use is 12 hours, with some extending to two days or more unless suitable protective clothing is worn. Check labels for this information.

Storage of Pesticides Read the label. Certain formulations or products have special storage requirements. Those restrictions or directions will be printed on the label.

- Make certain that the label is in good condition (readable) in order to know what is in the container and have directions for safe, effective and legal use.
- Never split volumes of pesticides into smaller containers. Containers for liquid formulations often are designed to filter

Required Signal Words by Toxicity Category

Categories	Signal Word Required on the Label	LD$_{50}$ Oral mg/kg	LD$_{50}$ Dermal mg/kg	LC$_{50}$ Inhalation mg/L	Probable Oral Lethal Dose for 150 lb. (68 kg) Man
I Highly toxic	DANGER (skull & crossbones) POISON	0–50	0–200	0–0.05	A few drops to a teaspoonful (5 ml)
II Moderately toxic	WARNING	>50–500	>200–2000	>0.05–0.5	More than 1 tsp. (5 ml) to 1 oz. (30 ml)
III Slightly toxic	CAUTION	>500–5000	>2000–5000	>0.5–5	Between 1 and 12 oz.(30 to 355 ml)
IV Least toxic	CAUTION	>5000	>5000	>5	More than 12 oz. (355 ml)

out ultraviolet (UV) light. Wettable powders and granular formulations often are sold in humidity-shielded bags.

- Write the purchase date on the label. Use older or opened products first. Products several years old may not be effective.
- Keep an up-to-date inventory of pesticides to assist in purchase decisions and in case of emergency.
- Usually, storage temperatures should not fall below freezing nor rise above 100 F (38 C). Ventilation is important for storage of most pesticides. Keep pesticides dry and out of direct sunlight.
- Store insecticides and fungicides away from herbicides to prevent use mix-up, contamination and possible plant damage. Never store pesticides with feed or seed.
- All entrances to pesticide-storage areas should be posted with warning signs instructing "Pesticides — Keep Out" and locked away from children, irresponsible adults and animals.

Disposal of Pesticide Containers

Federal laws have been established concerning pesticide container disposal.

Strict penalties can be administered against individuals disposing of containers in any manner that may endanger people, wildlife or the environment. Disposal instructions on the container label should be strictly followed. In addition, certain states and localities may have local laws concerning container disposal.

Several procedures must be followed regarding disposal:

- Thoroughly drain container in spray tank.
- Fill container approximately full, rinse thoroughly and pour into spray tank.
- Drain container into tank for 30 seconds.
- Rinse container three (3) times by adding water equivalent to 25 percent of the container volume. Cap container, shake and then empty into the tank.
- Follow any other pertinent label text dealing with disposal.
- A container that has been rinsed three times is considered solid waste.
- Wrap the container in newspaper, crush or puncture it to prevent reuse, then put it in a garbage can for disposal in an approved sanitary landfill.
- Never reuse any pesticide container for other purposes.

Orchid Pests

By Avas B. Hamon, PhD

NUMEROUS PESTS ARE KNOWN to attack orchids. However, the number of serious pests in the United States is small in comparison with the number of injurious pests associated with orchids throughout the world (Dekle and Kuitert, 1968).

Orchid growers should inspect their plants frequently. Learn how to recognize the more common pests that infest orchids; these are illustrated and discussed below.

INSECT PESTS

Scale Insects
(Coccoidea)

Scale insects are serious pests of orchids. They are so different from the usual concept of insects that they are frequently mistaken for fungal growths (Dekle and Kuitert, 1968). Scale insects are generally tiny inconspicuous animals that can become so numerous that they can cover the plants. They feed by means of their long stylets or mouthparts, causing the development of chlorotic areas wherever extraction of sap has occurred (Dekle and Kuitert, 1968).

Heavily infested plants appear unhealthy, and frequently symptoms are more obvious than the scale insects themselves. The presence of ants on a plant may be an indication that a soft scale or a mealybug infestation is present. Ants visit plants in search of honeydew, a sweetish liquid excreted by some scale insects. Honeydew is an excellent medium for sooty mold. Thus plants with ants and with sooty mold on the leaves should be examined carefully for soft scales and mealybugs.

As first instar nymphs, all scale insects are mobile and can crawl from plant to plant over short distances. Over long distances, they generally can be spread by the movement of infested plants.

The most important families of scale insects on orchids are:
- Armored Scales (family Diaspididae)
- Soft Scales (family Coccidae)
- Mealybugs (family Pseudococcidae)
- Pit Scales (family Asterolecaniidae)

Armored Scales
(Diaspididae)

Armored scales are found on the leaf, rhizome or pseudobulb. Infestations tend to develop beneath the leaf sheath, where they may be unnoticed for some time. Their presence may be indicated by yellowish discoloration of the leaves. Armored scale insects do not excrete honeydew and, therefore, are not attended by ants. These insects secrete a waxy, hardened covering that is not part of the insect body. The armor is nonliving and composed of secreted waxes incorporated with nymphal cast skins. This protective covering, under which the insect lives and feeds, is called the armor, hence the common name. Armor may be circular, semicircular, oblong or pear-shaped. The adult female is always wingless and legless, and the antennae are usually reduced to one segment with one or two setae. The female body varies in shape from circular to elongate and is from $1/8$ inch (1 to 3 mm) in length or diameter.

Male armor is usually of a different size and shape from the female's. In many species, the male armor is elongate, cylindrical, pupal caselike, white and ridged longitudinally. In other species, it may be shaped much like the female armor. Adult male scale insects have functional wings, look much like small gnats and are seldom observed. Their mouthparts are nonfunctional and adult males live only a few hours.

Products Registered for Use on Orchids

Pests		Insecticide and Formulation	Dosage 100 gal.	1 gal.
Aphids		Sprays		
	(C)	Insecticidal Soap	See label directions	
	(A)	Malathion, 50% EC	$1^{1}/_{4}$ pts. (592 ml)	$1^{1}/_{4}$ tsp. (6.2 ml)
	(C)	Mavrik Aquaflow	2–5 fl. oz.	—
	(C)	Orthene turf, tree & ornamental spray	$^{1}/_{3}$ lb. (151 gm)	1 tsp. (5 ml)
	(B)	Enstar II	See label directions	
	(C)	Marathon, 1% G	See label directions	
Beetles and Weevils		Sprays		
	(A)	Diazinon 50 W	1 lb. (454 gm)	1 Tbsp. (14.8 ml)
	(A)	Sevin 80 W SP	See label directions	
Mealybugs		Sprays		
	(A)	Malathion, 50% EC	$1^{1}/_{4}$ pts. (592 ml)	$1^{1}/_{4}$ tsp. (6.2 ml)
	(B)	Talstar 10 WP	6–16 oz.	
	(B)	Enstar 5E	See label directions	
	(C)	Marathon, 1% G	See label directions	
Mites		Sprays		
	(C)	Avid 0.15 EC	See label directions	
	(C)	Insecticidal Soap	See label directions	
	(C)	Mavrik Aquaflow	5 fl. oz (142 ml)	
	(B)	Talstar 10 WP	6–16 oz. (170–455 ml)	
Scales		Sprays		
	(A)	Malathion, 50% EC	$1^{1}/_{4}$ pts. (592 ml)	$1^{1}/_{4}$ tsp. (6.2 ml)
	(A)	Oil Sprays (Volck Oil/Sunspray)	See label directions	
	(C)	Knox Out 2 FM	See label directions	
	(C)	Orthene Turf, Tree and Ornamental Spray	$^{1}/_{3}$ lb. (151 gm)	1 tsp. (5 ml)
Snails and Slugs		Baits		
	(C)	Mesurol (Bait)	See label directions	
	(C)	Metaldehyde (Bait or Dust)	See label directions	
	(C)	Metaldehyde + Sevin Bait	See label directions	

*Labeled use code: (A) nongreenhouse, shadehouse and field only
(B) greenhouse only
(C) both greenhouse and nongreenhouse

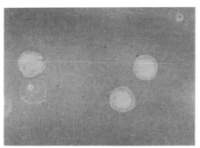

Of all scale insects that attack orchids, Boisduval scale is of the greatest economic importance. The female, shown here, has nearly circular armor that is thin, flat and dingy white to light yellow.

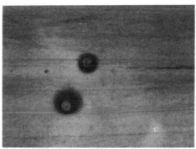

Female Florida red scale is similar to red orchid scale, but the armor of the latter is coarser.

Clusters of male Boisduval scale, which is elongate, has three longitudinal ridges and is snow white. Like other armored scales, it can be found on the leaf, rhizome or pseudobulb.

All armored scales are much alike in habits and life history. The female may deposit 30 to 150 eggs under the armor.

These may hatch in one or two weeks or longer, depending on the temperature. The young first instar scale insect (a crawler) is oval in shape and moves along the plant in search of a place to feed. It inserts its styletlike mouthparts into the plant and, in the case of the female, remains there for the rest of its life. The adult stage is reached in five to seven weeks. There are several generations per year (Dekle and Kuitert, 1968).

Species of major importance on orchids include the following:

Boisduval Scale [*Diaspis boisduvalii*]

Of all the scale insects on orchids this one is of the greatest economic impor-

tance (Dekle and Kuitert, 1968). The female armor is nearly circular, $^1/_{16}$ inch (1 to 2 mm) in diameter, thin, flat and dingy white to light yellow. The adult male armor is elongate, has three longitudinal ridges, and is less than $^1/_{16}$ inch (1 mm) long and snow white. Males usually occur in clusters and give the appearance of a cottony mass on the leaf. Because of this mass, they are readily recognizable (Hussey et al., 1969). Severe infestations of this scale induce darkened areas on the host and are difficult to control.

Florida Red Scale [*Chrysomphalus aonidum*]

The adult female armor is circular, $^1/_{16}$ inch (2 mm) in diameter, moderately convex, dark reddish brown to almost black and the margin is somewhat ash gray (Dekle and Kuitert, 1968). Exuviae (cast skins of first and second instars) are central and reddish brown, with a lighter ring around the first. The adult male armor is more elongate than the female, and the color is usually lighter.

Proteus Scale [*Parlatoria proteus*]

The adult female armor is elongate-oval, about $^1/_{16}$ inch (1 to 2 mm) long, slightly convex and a brownish or greenish yellow with lighter margins. The second exuvia is quite large, with a longitudinal ridge. Adult male armor is elongate, sides parallel, and less than $^1/_{16}$ inch

Female proteus scale. Dense colonies of proteus scale are frequently found at the leaf bases of orchids.

Adult female and nymphs of brown soft scale excrete large quantities of honeydew.

A waxy or dusty secretion is typical of vanda orchid scale, of which the female is shown here.

(1mm) long, and about the same color as the female armor. Dense colonies are frequently found at the leaf bases of orchids (Hussey et al., 1969).

Red Orchid Scale [*Furcaspis biformis*]

Female armor is nearly circular, convex, dark reddish brown and $^{1}/_{16}$ inch (1.5 to 2 mm) in diameter. The exuviae are central to subcentral, prominent and the same general color as the other parts of armor. Male armor is similar to female armor, but much smaller. Red orchid scale is similar to Florida red scale, but the armor texture is much coarser in the former.

Vanda Orchid Scale [*Genaparlatoria pseudaspidiotus*]

The female armor is oval, slightly to moderately convex, dark brown, $^{1}/_{16}$ inch (1 to 1.5 mm) long and is usually covered with a thin, waxy or dusty secretion. The male armor is similar in color to the female armor but much smaller.

Of all the armored scale insect species reported on orchids, only Boisduval and proteus scale are considered economically important. However, nearly all species have the potential of becoming serious if conditions are favorable.

Soft Scales
(Coccidae)

The soft scale insects do not have a detached protective armor like the armored scale insects. The body may be exposed or covered by soft wax, dull or glassy, clear or opaque, translucent or netlike, and variable in size and shape. Soft scales infest the leaf and pseudobulb. They feed as the armored scales do by sucking nutrients from the plant. Adult female soft scales have three pairs of legs and segmented antennae, but are wingless (Dekle and Kuitert, 1968).

Brown Soft Scale [*Coccus hesperidum*]

The female is oval, flat to slightly convex, and $^{1}/_{8}$ inch (1 to 3 mm) long. The color is yellowish green or yellowish brown, often flecked with brown spots. Parasitized specimens are convex, elongate and dark brown (Dekle and Kuitert, 1968). The underside of the adult female is concave, thus providing protection for the young scales that are born alive. Brown soft scale is widely distributed in greenhouses and outdoors in warmer

Stellate scale, a soft scale, is character-ized by its star-shaped bodies that resemble starfish. Adults and nymphs are shown here.

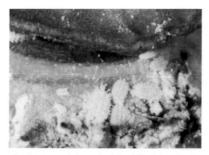

Orchid mealybug is identified by its 2- to 4-mm-long cottony white bodies aggregated into masses that are easily seen with the naked eye.

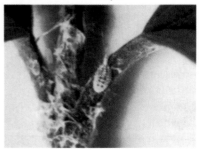

Adult and nymphs of striped mealybug, one of several mealybugs that cause minor infestations on orchids.

areas. Each generation requires about two months, and large quantities of honeydew are excreted (Westcott, 1964).

Stellate Scale [*Vinsonia stellifera*]

This soft scale is star-shaped and soft-bodied, resembling a miniature starfish (Dekle and Kuitert, 1968). The adult female is $^3/_8$ inch (4 to 5 mm) across the median ray. The convex, waxy, protective cover is glassy and semitransparent; rays become flattened at their extremities. The live female is pink to purplish red and darkens with age to a reddish brown.

Stellate scale was found in Florida in 1953. This infestation was successfully eradicated; however, it has been intercept-ed many times since then by the Plant Protection and Quarantine Division at Miami and for this reason is included here (Anon., 1979).

Mealybugs
(Pseudococcidae)

Mealybugs do not form scale coverings like the armored scales but are not exposed like some of the soft scales. They are soft-bodied and partially or entirely covered with, or enclosed in, a waxy, cottony or feltlike secretion. Adult females are generally oval in shape and from $^1/_{16}$ to $^3/_8$ inches (2 to 5 mm) long. They all have well-developed legs and anten-nae in the immature stages, and most mealybugs retain the appendages

and power to move about throughout life. Mealybugs usually appear white, as their pinkish or yellowish body color is obscured by the mealy wax secretions. Like the soft scales, they excrete honey-dew in large amounts, and this attracts ants and serves as a medium for the devel-opment of sooty molds.

Orchid Mealybug [*Pseudococcus microcirculus*]

This mealybug is about $^1/_{16}$ to $^3/_8$ inch-es (2 to 4 mm) long, smoothly covered with mealy wax with no definite bare areas visible. There is a series of wax fila-ments along the body margin, with the posterior filaments about twice as long. The females deposit eggs in white cottony ovisacs. Each female will lay 100 to 200 pale yellow eggs that hatch in about two weeks, and then the crawlers disperse. The complete life cycle requires two-and-one-half months.

Diligent use of a systemic insecticide is required to eradicate infestations of orchid pit scale, because the insect's waxy covering repels pesticides sprayed onto it. Shown here are an adult female and nymphs.

Other Mealybug Species

There are several other mealybugs that infest orchids, but they are considered minor pests. They include the longtailed mealybug (*Pseudococcus longispinus*) and the striped mealybug (*Ferrisia virgata*). The longtailed mealybug is slightly smaller than the orchid mealybug, but can be distinguished from it by the long posterior filaments.

Pit Scales
(Asterolecaniidae)

The pit scales secrete a waxy test or covering and the females live within this wax covering. Pit scales may cause host plants to produce pits or callous tissue around the pit scale insects. However, I have not observed callous tissue on orchid plants. Damage is by direct removal of sap by the scale insects styletlike mouth parts.

Orchid Pit Scale [*Asterolecanium epidendri*]

The orchid pit scale is an occasional problem on orchids in Florida and other parts of the world. The female test or wax covering is slightly longer than wide or nearly circular. The natural size is about $1/16$ inch (1.5 mm) in diameter. The wax covering is relatively flat and is usually greenish, pale yellow or transparent. Marginal wax filaments may be pale gold-

Orchid pit scale is obvious on this orchid that shows symptoms resulting from a large infestation — unsightly chlorotic spots on an unhealthy plant.

en to medium pink. These wax filaments appear to be arranged in groups. Damage from this scale insect appears to be minimal if few scales are present; however, large numbers will cause unsightly chlorotic spots and overall, an unhealthy plant. Controls are difficult because of the waxy covering and require diligent use of a systemic insecticide.

Control of scale insects in general is a difficult proposition. The armored scales are protected from insecticides by the hard armor, and many of the soft scale insects and mealybugs are protected by other types of wax. Because of this wax protection, it is generally advisable to apply controls when the unprotected crawler (first instar) is present.

Thrips
(Thysanoptera)

Thrips are occasionally serious orchid pests. They are minute insects, less than $1/16$ to $3/8$ inches (0.5 to 5 mm) long, with straplike wings fringed with long cilia.

41

Thrips feed by rasping the plant cells and sucking up the exuding juices. Thrips are important pests not only for the mechanical injury that their feeding causes, but for being vectors of bacterial, fungal and viral diseases (Kona and Papp, 1977). Orchid growers are most likely to encounter species that attack the flower. Infested buds fail to open properly or the flowers are deformed. Feeding sites on the flowers turn brown and the petals become streaked and discolored.

Thrips are active, and when alarmed will turn up the abdomen tip as if to sting. The tiny eggs are laid on and in plant tissues. Each female lays from 25 to 50 eggs, which hatch in several days to three weeks. Two to four weeks later adult thrips appear. Normally there are three to five generations per year; however, some species have one generation per year.

Cuban Laurel Thrips [*Gynaikothrips ficorum*]

These are light yellow in the immature stages, and the adult is dark brown to black (Denmark, 1967a). Adults are $^1/_8$ inch (2.5 to 3.5 mm) long and move rapidly when disturbed. These thrips may bite people (Denmark, 1967a).

Flower Thrips [*Frankliniella bispinosa*]

This is a pest of many plants (including orchids) in the South, where it damages the flowers. The adult has an orange head and thorax and lemon yellow abdomen (Westcott, 1964). The larva is similar in color but paler than the adult and lacks wings. When disturbed, the abdomen may curl over the back as if to sting; however, thrips cannot sting.

Greenhouse Thrips [*Heliothrips haemorrhoidalis*]

These are about $^3/_8$ inch (1.8 mm) long with a strongly reticulate and blackish brown body with the posterior end lighter (Hussey et al., 1969). The legs and eight-segmented antennae are pale yellow, and the wings are slightly clouded but without

Thrips are minute insects that feed by rasping the plant cells and sucking up the exuding juices. Nymphs of the red-banded thrip are shown here.

bands (Westcott, 1964). Eggs are inserted singly in plant tissue, producing blisters (Denmark, 1967b). Young larvae are whitish with red eyes, and their bodies turn yellowish after feeding (Denmark, 1967b). According to Denmark (1967b), this species first feeds on the lower leaf surface and then moves to the upper surface when the population increases. Damage will appear as silvery or bleached leaves, wilting and dying, and in addition, leaves will be spotted with reddish black droplets of excrement (Denmark, 1967b; Westcott, 1964). Ranging worldwide, this species occurs outdoors in California, Florida, Georgia and in similar warm climates and in greenhouses in other states.

Orchid Thrips [*Chaetanophothrips orchidii* and *C. signipennis*]

These species are $^1/_{16}$ inch (1.2mm) long, yellow and devoid of sculpturing (Hussey et al., 1969). The antennae are yellow with the exception of the apices of segments IV and V, the apical half of VI, and all of VII and VIII, which are brown (Hussey et al., 1969). The forewings are brownish with a pale crossband at the base and another at the apex.

Red-banded Thrips [*Selenothrips rubrocinctus*]

The adult female is about $^1/_{16}$ inch (1.5 mm) long and has a dark brown to black body (Denmark, 1971). Legs are dark brown with the tips of femora and all

Springtails often occur on the surface of potting media or other decaying vegetable matter.

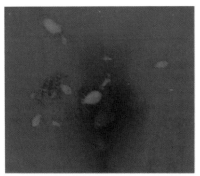

Aphids feed on plant juices, causing tender plant growth to become stunted and distorted. These small, soft-bodied insects live in colonies and excrete large amounts of honeydew where sooty molds develop.

of the tarsi yellow-white. The first three abdominal segments of the immature stages have a red pigment, hence the common name, red-banded thrips.

Control usually involves the use of the organic phosphate insecticides, which are toxic to thrips. In most cases, diazinon or malathion will give adequate control. If phytotoxic effects are suspected, tests should be carried out on only a few plants before applying to all plants. Spraying should be carried out under dry conditions but not in bright sunlight, and sheath-leaved plants should be drained after spraying (Hussey et al., 1969).

The black twig borer is a beetle with a hard body and chewing mouthparts.

Springtails
(Collembola)

Springtails are small insects that rarely exceed $^3/_8$ inch (5 mm) in length. They often occur in great numbers on the surface of potting media or other decaying vegetable matter. They are elongate with soft, rounded bodies and distinct heads. Springtails are usually milky white or gray; however, other variously colored species are known. They are seldom noticed unless especially numerous. These primitive insects do not have wings but propel themselves by means of a forked muscular appendage at the tip of the abdomen which is used to spring into the air. Springtails feed on decaying plant material, fungi, bacteria, algae and pollen. They are usually nuisance pests when they occur in large numbers.

Aphids
(Aphididae)

Aphids, or plant lice, are small, soft-bodied insects that live in colonies. They have sucking mouthparts and feed on plant juices. As a result of the continuous draining of plant juices, the tender growth becomes stunted and distorted. Aphids cause damage by removal of sap, by excreting large amounts of honeydew where sooty molds develop and by the toxic action of salivary secretions. Furthermore, they can introduce pathogens that cause disease, including viruses.

43

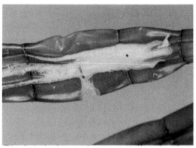

Black twig borer, known as the dendrobium beetle to orchid growers in Florida, bores into the canes of dendrobiums.

Small shot-holes in the stems of dendrobiums indicate the presence of the black twig borer. A yellowish area usually surrounds the shot-hole when the hole is newly made.

Aphids are less than $^1/_{16}$ to $^1/_4$ inch (1 to 6 mm) long, pear-shaped, whitish, greenish, yellowish, black or brown. They are slow-moving and usually have a pair of hornlike processes (cornicles) on the posterior end of the abdomen. The rates of development and reproduction are rapid and many generations may be produced in a year. Another peculiarity of aphid reproduction is that in most generations all individuals are females which reproduce parthenogenetically (without mating). When colonies become overcrowded or the plants harden, winged forms may appear, and these fly to other orchids and establish new colonies.

The pseudobulbs of cattleyas usually develop a rot following an attack by the black twig borer. A chlorotic area is always present around the infestation. Although the beetle does not kill plants, it detracts from the plants' aesthetic value.

Cotton Aphid, Melon Aphid [*Aphis gossypii*]

This aphid is troublesome on the buds and flowers. It is yellowish green to blackish green and is $^1/_{16}$ inch (1.2 mm) long. The cotton aphid is cosmopolitan and occurs on a wide range of hosts.

Macrosiphum luteum

Infestations of this yellowish to tan aphid are found on the leaf and stem. This species was introduced and has become established in Florida.

Beetles
(Coleoptera)

These insects usually have hard bodies and chewing mouthparts. The first pair of wings (elytra) are hard and cover the second pair which are membranous and used for flight. Many of the most destructive pests known to man are found in this group of insects. Only one species is of serious consequence to growers in Florida.

Black Twig Borer [*Xylosandrus compactus*]

This ambrosia beetle has been known as the dendrobium beetle to Florida orchid growers. It is a small, dark brown beetle about $^1/_8$ inch (4 mm) in length and is probably one of the most abundant scolytids in the tropical lowlands of the

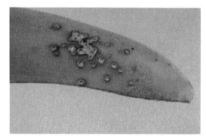

The orchidfly, technically a wasp, lays its eggs in plant tissue, in which the larvae feed and cause damage.

Americas and West Indies. It bores into the canes of *Dendrobium* species and also attacks the pseudobulbs of *Cattleya*. Small shot-holes on a plant indicate the presence of this insect. A yellowish area usually surrounds the shot-hole when dendrobiums are attacked. Pseudobulbs of cattleyas usually develop a rot following attack. A chlorotic area is always present around the infestation. Infestations of the beetle do not kill the plant but detract from its aesthetic value. This beetle also attacks a variety of other hosts. After emergence from the parent gallery and dispersal by flight, the young mature beetle enters the cane and constructs new galleries. It introduces spores of the "ambrosia" fungus, and the female lays eggs in the galleries. The generations appear to overlap, and a mixture of different life stages is usually present. Food of both larvae and adults is the fungi growing on the walls of the galleries.

Ants
(Hymenoptera)

Whenever ants are observed on an orchid, the plant should be examined carefully for soft scale insects, mealybugs and aphids. Ants actively drive away natural enemies of these pests, which allows the soft scales, mealybugs and aphids to multiply apparently unrestricted. Control of ants will aid greatly in the reduction and spread of these pests. Baygon, Dursban and diazinon give effective control of ants. Spray

should be applied to bench legs and at bases of walls, both inside and outside. Follow directions on these labels for ant control and avoid spraying orchids at these concentrations.

Wasps
(Hymenoptera)

A clear-winged chalcid wasp has been observed occasionally in orchid houses. It is known as the orchidfly, *Eurytoma orchidearum*, but it is not a true fly. This small $^1/_8$ inch (1.5 to 3 mm) long wasp inserts its eggs into the plant tissue. Injury is caused by the larvae feeding within the plant tissue. Pupation takes place in the cavity eaten out by the larvae, and the adult wasp cuts its way out of the cavity. Enlarged swollen pseudobulbs and exit holes are characteristic symptoms of plants attacked by this pest. Young pseudobulbs may be killed with a single attack; continued attacks may kill the parent plant. The orchids most commonly attacked are species and hybrids of *Cattleya, Epidendrum* and *Laelia*.

Cockroaches
(Orthoptera)

Cockroaches occasionally damage orchid flowers. They are nocturnal insects and hide during the day in sheltered, darkened places. Commonly referred to as waterbugs or palmetto bugs, cockroaches have a characteristic body appearance that makes them easy to distinguish from other insects. They vary in size and color, but generally they are broadly oval, flattened and have long antennae and chewing mouthparts. In Florida, cockroaches are found commonly outdoors in large numbers. They crawl through cracks or under doors to enter orchid houses.

Caterpillars
(Lepidoptera)

Caterpillars are the immature stages of

45

Borer damage by lepidoptera evident on a pseudobulb. Caterpillars begin feeding immediately upon hatching and continue feeding until the pupal stage is reached.

Although fungus gnats usually feed on fungi and decaying organic materials, they may occur in large enough numbers to be considered a nuisance. Larvae are shown here.

moths and butterflies. They are frequently referred to as worms. All caterpillars have chewing mouthparts, usually three pairs of true legs on the front of the body, and usually four pairs of unjointed, soft, fleshy projections called prolegs on the abdomen with a fifth pair, the anal prolegs, at the posterior end. The body is usually cylindrical in shape and varies from slender to robust.

The life cycle of moths and butterflies is divided into four distinct stages: egg, destructive caterpillar or larva, pupa or resting stage, and adult. Adult females usually lay their eggs on the host plants. The caterpillars begin feeding immediately upon hatching and continue feeding until the pupal stage is reached. During the pupal stage transformation to the adult moth or butterfly takes place.

Darkwinged Fungus Gnats
(Diptera)

Darkwinged fungus gnats feed on fungi and decaying organic material and are not usually an economic problem (Mead, 1978). In large numbers they may be considered a nuisance. A few species are known to attack healthy greenhouse plants including young orchids (Mead, 1978).

The adults are delicate flies with dark brown bodies, dusky wings, small head, moderately prominent eyes, threadlike antennae and relatively long legs. The young, or maggots, are whitish with black heads, legless and about $^1/_4$ inch (6 mm) long when fully grown.

Cultural controls include removing rotting organic materials and avoiding overwatering of potted plants. Apply a diazinon soil drench. All areas in the greenhouse should be sprayed, particularly those with soil, such as under benches (Mead, 1978). Use Resmethrin 1 percent aerosol against the adult gnats.

Orchid Blossom Midge [*Contarinia aculipennis*] See page 120

NONINSECT PESTS

Snails and Slugs
(Stylommatophora)

Snails and slugs may be found almost everywhere but, in general, they prefer habitats offering shelter, adequate moisture and an abundant food supply including lime for snails (Burch, 1960). Land snails and slugs are nocturnal, but following a rain they may come out of their hiding places in the daylight. Lower temperature and higher moisture are the main factors to account for their nocturnal habits, not the presence of darkness (Burch, 1960).

During the day, snails and slugs can be found under old boards and logs, under

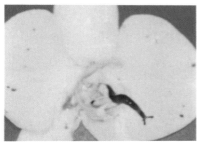

Slugs are among the most serious orchid pests and usually feed only on the buds and flowers. In Florida, the marsh slug, shown here, is the most commonly reported slug on orchids.

bricks and stones, among hedge rows, and beneath damp refuse and litter (Burch, 1960). They move with a gliding motion on a long, flat muscular organ called the foot. Mucus is secreted by glands in the foot, making movement easier, and because of this mucus a characteristic slime trail is left wherever they go (Dekle and Kuitert, 1968).

Snails and slugs are among the most serious orchid pests and feed on the buds and flowers (Jefferson and Morishita, 1975). In some situations they are known to feed on other plant parts (Dekle and Kuitert, 1968). The marsh slug (*Deroceras laeve*) is the most commonly reported slug on orchids in Florida.

The control of snails and slugs must include sanitation, that is, the destruction of hiding places and removal of excess refuse. Chemical controls are Mesural (bait), metaldehyde (bait or dust), and metaldehyde and Sevin (bait). Consult the label for directions and precautions.

Mites
(Acari)

Mites are closely related to ticks, spiders and scorpions. Some species spin fine strands of silk similar to those of spiders (Dekle and Kuitert, 1968). The two-spotted mite (*Tetranychus urticae*) and the phalaenopsis mite (*Tenuipalpus pacificus*) are commonly encountered on orchids (Dekle and Kuitert, 1968). Mites are large enough to be visible; however, their presence is usually not suspected until considerable damage has occurred (Jefferson and Morishita, 1975). The presence of mites can be determined by rubbing a white cloth over the suspected infestation. If mites or eggs are present, brownish streaks will be seen on the cloth (Dekle and Kuitert, 1968).

Mites damage orchids by removing sap and chlorophyll with their needle-like mouthparts. According to Dekle and Kuitert (1968), the withdrawal of chlorophyll results in the characteristic blanching and silverlike appearance of the leaf.

Brevipalpus californicus

The first observable injury from this mite feeding on orchid leaves appears as silvery areas that eventually become sunken and brown (Jeppson et al., 1975). Heavily infested leaves will become yellow and drop from the plants. Individuals of *B. californicus* are difficult to see because they lie flat against the leaf and move slowly; however, populations can be detected by the presence of cast skins (Jeppson et al., 1975).

Phalaenopsis Mite [*Tenuipalpus pacificus*]

This is one of the false spider mites, and, unlike the true spider mites, they do not spin webs (Jefferson and Morishita, 1975). This mite is a pest in California, Florida, Panama and some European countries (Jeppson, Keifer, and Baker, 1975). Feeding by these mites causes dark spots on leaves and eventual necrosis of tissue. According to Jeppson et al. (1975), this mite has a slow development; the incubation period requires 18 to 23 days, and each of the developmental stages 14 to 15 days; therefore, the life cycle is at least 64 days.

The presence of mites is usually not suspected until considerable damaged has occurred. Stippling, blanching and a silverlike appearance to the foliage are characteristic symptoms.

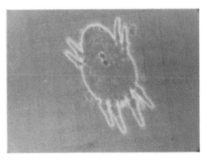

The phalaenopsis mite, enlarged here x200, is a false spider mite and, therefore, does not spin a web.

Two-spotted Spider Mite [*Tetranychus urticae*]

This mite is pale green or yellow with a dark spot on each side. If the infestation is heavy, webbing will be apparent (Jefferson and Morishita, 1975). According to Dekle and Kuitert (1968), an adult female two-spotted spider mite will lay three to five eggs per day and may lay several hundred during her life.

Millipedes
(Thousand-legged worms)

Millipedes possess a head, a thoracic region of three segments, and an abdomen or trunk region of many segments each bearing two pairs of legs, hence the common name thousand-legged worms. The body is very hard and when disturbed will frequently coil up like a watch spring (Hussey et al., 1969). Millipedes live within soils and humus where they feed mainly on dead plant material (Hussey et al., 1969); however, they have on occasion damaged young roots of orchid seedlings (Jefferson and Morishita, 1975). As with sowbugs and springtails, moisture is the critical factor influencing their life and habits. Therefore, avoiding excess moisture is important in preventing infestations of millipedes. Where chemical controls are needed, areas can be sprayed with diazinon or applied as a pot drench.

Nematodes

There are many types of soil and waterborne nematodes called "eel worms" that are harmless to plants; however, some nematodes are parasitic on plants. Among those that infect plant tissue, there are those that invade roots, stems and flower buds (Northen, 1970).

Reported instances of nematode infestations in orchids are rare, and this is because normal cultural conditions are not conducive to nematode development (personal communication, R. P. Esser). Instances reported in the literature include: a species that attacks the flower bud of terete vandas in Hawaii (Northen, 1970); Scribner's root lesion nematode on *Cymbidium* in California, where the symptoms were poor growth, yellowing of outer leaves and reduction of flowering (Sher, 1959); and another that infects leaves of *Cymbidium* and other orchids in New Zealand (Northen, 1970).

ORCHID PEST CONTROL

Over the years, improvements in transportation have contributed to the movement of orchids. This has increased the likelihood of a serious pest's being intro-

Damage caused by phalaenopsis mites, which are reported from California, Florida, Panama and some European countries.

Millipedes live within soils and humus where they feed mainly on dead plant materials. However, there are reports of their damaging the young roots of orchid seedlings. Preventing an accumulation of excess moisture helps ward off infestations of millipedes.

duced and gaining a foothold before being discovered and brought under control (Dekle and Kuitert, 1968). A successful program to prevent introductions requires thorough inspection at the point of origin, a well-informed plant inspection service at the point of entry and the cooperation of concerned travelers having specimen plants.

The most common pests of orchids are the same pests that attack many of our ornamentals and have a wide host range (Jefferson and Morishita, 1975). Because companion plants can act as reservoirs of orchid pests, they should be removed from the orchid house. Removal of these plants from positions close to orchids contributes to the prevention of pest infestations.

Another important method of prevention is sanitation. Ground covers and debris around the greenhouse or lath house can harbor pests such as snails and slugs. According to Jefferson and Morishita (1975), infestations of many pests often originate on nearby plants and may spread into the greenhouse. Landscaping around the greenhouse or lath house is not desirable because of this pest problem.

Pesticides developed in recent years are quite specific in their action and the pests they control, as contrasted with the early broad-spectrum pesticides. In most crop situations the trend is definitely away from preventive treatments in pest control; however, in greenhouse crops with high value, such as orchids, some degree of preventive measures is desirable.

Many amateurs and commercial growers hire a professional pest control operator, and this has many advantages (Jefferson and Morishita, 1975). For the grower who decides to do his or her own pest control, many decisions are necessary. When deciding on the type and timing of controls most likely to be successful, a knowledge of the pest's biology is essential. If pesticides are to be used it is necessary to choose the best chemical, type of formulation, method and time and frequency of application in relation to the life history of the pest. Consideration should be given to the presence of other pests that may be controlled at the same time. The safety of workers also must not be overlooked. The occurrence of chemical resistance in some pests adds to the difficulty of selecting effective control measures (Hussey et al., 1969). Also, chemical applications may be a major factor in upsetting a natural balance; knowledge of the effect of pesticide treatments on subsequent pest infestations may aid in providing the most economical control (Jeppson et al., 1975).

49

PHYTOTOXICITY

Some chemicals used as pesticides cause plant injury when applied to certain varieties or when used at concentrations higher than recommended. Accuracy of dosage is important when using pesticides to minimize the danger of plant injury. The extent of plant injury depends on temperature, humidity and many other environmental factors.

Dimethoate (Cygon) has consistently caused injury to several kinds of orchids. Most orchid are tolerant of malathion. If information is not readily available on how a pesticide affects your particular orchids, a few plants should be carefully tested before general application.

Orthene 15.6% EC (emulsifiable concentrate) apparently will cause crippled flowers on several kinds of orchids. Davidson (1982) has reported that only Orthene 75% SP (sprayable powder) is recommended by the Ortho Agricultural Chemicals Division of the Chevron Chemical Company for use on orchids in the greenhouse.

References

Anonymous. 1979. *List of Intercepted Plant Pests, July 1, 1973-Sept. 30, 1977.* PPQ-APHIS, U. S. Department of Agriculture, Washington, D. C.

Burch, J. B. *Some Snails and Slugs of Quarantine Significance to the United States.* ARS, U. S. Department of Agriculture, Washington, D.C.

Davidson, O. W. 1982. Orthene insecticide — be careful how you use it! *Amer. Orchid Soc. Bull.* 51:512.

Dekle, G. W., and L. C. Kuitert. 1968. *Orchid Insects, Related Pests, and Control.* Division of Plant Industry, Florida Department of Agriculture, Tallahassee, Florida.

Denmark, H. A. 1967a. Cuban-laurel thrips, *Gynaikothrips ficorum,* in Florida. *Florida Dept. Agric., Division of Plant Industry, Ent. Circ.* 59:1-2.

___.1967b. The greenhouse thrips in Florida. *Florida Dept. Agric., Division of Plant Industry, Ent. Circ.* 64:1.

___ .1971. The red-banded thrips, Selenothrips rubrocinctus (Giard.). *Florida Dept. Agric., Division of Plant Industry, Ent. Circ.* 108:1-2.

Hussey, N. W., W. H. Read, and J. J. Hesling. 1969. *The Pests of Protected Cultivation: The Biology and Control of Glasshouse and Mushroom Pests.* American Elsevier Publishing Co., New York.

Jefferson, R. N., and F. S. Morishita. 1975. Orchid pests. Pages 2-14 in *Handbook on Orchid Pests and Diseases.* American Orchid Society, Cambridge, Massachusetts.

Jeppson, L. R., H. H. Keifer, and E. W. Baker. 1975. *Mites Injurious to Economic Plants.* University of California Press, Berkeley, California.

Kono, T., and C. S. Papp. 1977. *Handbook of Agricultural Pests.* California Department of Food and Agriculture, Division of Plant Industry, Laboratory Services — Entomology.

Mead, F. W. 1978. Darkwinged fungus gnats, *Bradysia* spp., in Florida greenhouses. *Florida Dept. Agric. and Cons. Serv., Division of Plant Industry, Ent. Circ.* 186:1-4.

Northen, R. T. 1970. *Home Orchid Growing.* Van Nostrand Reinhold Co., New York.

Sher, S. A. 1959. Nematodes on ornamentals. *Calif. Agric.* 13:21-22.

Westcott, C. 1964. *The Gardener's Bug Book.* Doubleday & Co., Garden City, New York.

This is Contribution No. 564, Entomology Section, Bureau of Entomology, Nematology, and Plant Pathology, Florida Department of Agriculture & Consumer Services, Gainesville, Florida.

Diseases Caused by Bacteria and Fungi

By Gary W. Simone, PhD, and Harry C. Burnett, PhD

IT IS THE NATURAL ORDER FOR every plant to have a requisite number of pests and pathogens that attack it. Orchids are no exception to this rule. In the United States, there are in excess of 130 reported plant diseases affecting one or more orchid genera, caused by such pathogens as nematodes, fungi, bacteria and viruses. The more common diseases caused by fungi, bacteria and nematodes will be dealt with here.

An overview of the symptoms, pathogen biology and management strategies for the most common orchid diseases is given here in an effort to assist commercial and hobbyist growers. No one person will ever encounter all of these diseases nor become proficient at diagnosing them all. Remember that, due to the microscopic size of the causal agents of these diseases and the similarity in their symptomatology, visual diagnoses are often erroneous. The best source of diagnostic assistance will be the plant-disease diagnostic clinic in your state. These facilities are commonly associated with the Federal Cooperative Extension Service and Plant Pathology departments at "land grant" universities. Similar facilities may exist in state regulatory agencies or in the private sector as well.

Bacterial soft rot caused by *Erwinia carotovora* pv. *carotovora* and *Erwinia chrysanthemi* on a phalaenopsis.

Survey of Diseases

The plant diseases affecting the Orchidaceae range from root diseases to stem/pseudobulb decays, leaf spots to flower blights. Generally, those diseases affecting the roots, stem and pseudobulbs cause the most damage. The plant pathogens involved in these diseases, although slower to develop, are also more difficult to diagnose. Additionally, these pathogens have extensive internal growth (some becoming systemic) within the orchid plant, resulting in a slower, more difficult curative control program with systemic fungicides. These diseases, if not diagnosed and treated early, can cause plant decline to death. By contrast, the more numerous group of pathogens affecting leaves and flowers, although cosmetically bothersome, are usually not so severe as to cause plant death. These more superficial diseases can also be effectively controlled through sanitation of infected plant parts, which serves to both remove the cosmetic injury on the plant and to eradicate the pathogen from the host. The best method to produce a disease-free orchid collection is to implement an integrated disease-management strategy.

Disease control in the past has emphasized pesticide use, both preventively and curatively. This general philosophy has dramatically shifted away from routine pesticide use to one of "use as needed." The primary reason for this new outlook is the growing public perception of enhanced exposure to pesticides in both the landscape and the food chain. Whether this perception is correct is not at issue. This change in attitude is fostering a greater awareness of integrated pest management in all production systems as well as in the urban environment.

There are definite benefits associated with the "use when needed" philosophy for pesticides. The use of these pesticides is now swinging back to one of a specialized production tool for the emergency situation, such as a fungicide for a plant-disease outbreak, rather than as a routine production tool that compensates for imprecise and loosely managed horticulture. Additional benefits of reduced pesticide use as relates to fungicides are:

■ Decreased production costs.
■ Decreased worker exposure to fungicides in the greenhouse.
■ Decreased risk of chronic plant injury from repeated, scheduled fungicide use.
■ Decreased risk of plant injury from pesticide interactions.
■ Decreased risk of tolerant or resistant pathogen development.

Perhaps the most important long-range benefit of reduced, more managed use of fungicides is to extend the labeled availability of these products for specialty crops like orchids. Hopefully, more conservative usage of the presently available fungicides listed on pages 70–73 will preserve them for producers and hobbyists alike in the future.

Plant-disease Profiles

In excess of 100 species of fungi and bacteria have been reported in technical literature or plant-disease indices in the United States. The majority of these plant pathogens are infrequently encountered and are therefore of little economic or aesthetic concern. The more common and important disease problems across the diverse orchid genera will be summarized in a series of plant disease profiles. Each profile will highlight the common disease name, pathogen name, host range, distribution, symptoms and a disease-management strategy. The diseases are grouped

---

Preventing Diseases

The following steps represent a balanced disease-management program:

■ Adopt the optimal horticulture for orchid genera grown. Cultural stress can predispose plants to plant diseases. Water when needed and at a time that allows rapid drying of foliage. Fertilize regularly to maintain plant vigor. Repot orchids as needed (at least every two years).
■ Purchase only disease-free plants.
■ Always segregate new plant additions (four to six weeks) beyond splash distance from the existing collection and at the end of the air-circulation pattern in a greenhouse.
■ Avoid mixing orchid collections with nonrelated plant species that may host potential disease-causing microbes.
■ Inspect plants weekly during cultural activities. Carefully examine all newly acquired plants, plants along air-intake areas (doors, walkways), as well as those in condensation pockets within the greenhouse.
■ Sanitize localized disease symptoms (leaf spots, flower blights) at first appearance. Keep floors and benches free of plant debris.
■ Use fungicides when needed.

---

based on the plant part of the orchid that is damaged:

■ Root Stem and Pseudobulb Rots
■ Leaf Spots
■ Flower Blights

ROOTS, STEM AND PSEUDOBULB ROTS

Anthracnose See Leaf Spots

Early lesion development of black rot on an orchid.

Bacterial Soft Rot [Erwinia carotovora subsp. carotovora and Erwinia chrysanthemi]

Hosts *Erwinia carotovora* pv. *carotovora* is reported from *Aliceara, Ascocentrum, Cattleya, Chondrorhyncha, Cycnoches, Cymbidium, Cyrtopodium, Grammatophyllum, Laelia, Laeliocattleya, Lockhartia, Miltonia, Oncidium, Phaius, Phalaenopsis* and *Vanda.* Additionally, *E. carotovora* subsp. *carotovora* has a broad host range of nonorchid plants including those in such economically important families as the cabbage, cucumber and potato families as well as a wide array of flowering and foliage ornamentals.

The second species, *E. chrysanthemi,* is reported from only *Phalaenopsis.* This bacterial pathogen is common on such flowering and foliage ornamentals as *Aechmea, Aglaonema, Ananas, Begonia, Chrysanthemum, Colocasia, Dahlia, Dianthus, Dieffenbachia, Euphorbia pulcherrima, Philodendron, Saintpaulia* and *Syngonium* spp. The orchid genera *Brassocattleya, Dendrobium, Doritaenopsis, Doritis, Odontoglossum, Paphiopedilum* and *Myrmechophila* (syn. *Schomburgkia*) also have reported soft-rot diseases, but pathogen speciation is not available.

Distribution Both bacteria are worldwide, being especially important in the warm climates.

Symptoms Environmental conditions

Bacterial brown rot caused by *Erwinia cypripedii* on paphiopedilum seedlings. The first symptoms are small, round to oval, water-soaked spots, often near the middle of the leaf. As the disease progresses, the color of the spot changes from a light brown to a very dark chestnut brown, as seen here.

that favor these soft-rot diseases are warm- to hot-temperature periods with plentiful moisture. These bacteria are common epiphytes on the leaf surface and aggressive invaders of wounded tissue. Bacteria rely on rain or irrigation splash for plant-to-plant movement. Infection results in a dark, greyish-green lesion that rapidly enlarges. Affected areas are soft decayed, brown in color and offensive smelling. Decay spreads most rapidly in leaves and roots and more slowly in rhizomes and pseudobulbs.

Management Purchase only pathogen-free plants or propagules. Remember to isolate new stock for at least four weeks. When propagating, use a different, sterilized cutting instrument per plant. Allow the unused cutters to rest in rubbing alcohol between uses. If plants or divisions are routinely dipped before planting, make sure the dip solution temperature is equal to or greater than the plant temperatures to avoid vacuum infiltration of plant surface-borne bacteria. When disease does occur, isolate and sanitize these plants. Reduce watering frequency to minimize leaf wetness. Apply sprays of Physan or Captan as bactericides. Copper sulfate-based fungicides are also effective against bacteria, but may be damaging to certain genera, especially when bloom is present or when temperatures exceed 90 F (32 C).

Black Rot [*Pythium ultimum* and *Phytophthora cactorum*]

This fungal disease complex represents the most damaging disease of orchids and is caused by two related water molds that are most aggressive during high moisture periods. *Pythium ultimum* favors temperatures between 50 and 72 F (10 and 22 C), while *Phytophthora cactorum* favors a range of 50 to 68 F (10 to 20 C) for reproduction.

Hosts Both fungi are reported from *Ascocenda, Brassavola, Brassocattleya, Brassolaeliocattleya, Cattleya, Cyrtopodium, Dendrobium, Epidendrum, Laeliocattleya, Oncidium, Phaius, Sophrolaeliocattleya* and *Vanda. Pythium ultimum* is also reported from *Bothriochilus, Brassia, Coelogyne, Cymbidium, Huntleya, Laelia, Renanthera* and *Vuylstekeara. Phytophthora cactorum* is also reported from *Aerides, Ascocentrum, Epicattleya, Galeandra, Gongora, Maxillaria, Paphiopedilum, Potinara, Rhynchostylis, Rodriguezia, Trichocentrum* and *Trichocidium.* Nonorchid hosts of *P. cactorum* include 154 plant genera in 54 families. *Pythium ultimum* also has a wide host range that includes *Aglaonema, Begonia, Calceolaria, Euphorbia, Saintpaulia, Senecio* and *Sinningia.*

Distribution *Phytophthora cactorum* is widespread in temperate areas while *P. ultimum* is cosmopolitan.

Symptoms Two phases of this disease can occur involving one or both pathogens. A damping-off disease may develop in pots of seedlings as the fungus invades the seedlings at soil line, producing water-soaked lesions that enlarge rapidly, causing seedling death. Mature plants can also be invaded at any plant part. Cattleyas are especially susceptible. The fungus can be introduced through

Although fusarium wilt caused by *Fusarium oxysporum* f. *cattleyae* can cause plants to die in three to nine weeks, plants generally live a year or longer in a state of continuing decline. Here, a *Cattleya*-like orchid exhibits symptoms.

unsterile pots, media or water sources as well as water-splash from adjacent infested pots. Infection produces a dark-to-black lesion on roots, stems or leaves. Leaf lesions are soft and may be one-sided on the leaf. Lesions expand and, if they reach the crown, will girdle and kill the entire plant.

Management Avoid use of unsterile media and pots. Do not irrigate from shallow, surface bodies of water, such as ponds and canals. Where orchids are placed outdoors in the summer, keep them on a solid, nonsoil surface or elevated 3 to 4 feet (90 to 120 cm) off the ground to avoid splash contamination. At first disease appearance, segregate infected plants. Sanitize leaf spots before fungus reaches the crown. Minimize the duration and frequency of leaf wetness. If disease is diagnosed early, drenches of the protectant fungicides Truban or Terrazole will be effective. As disease develops, use systemic fungicides like Aliette or Subdue for effective control.

Brown Rot [*Erwinia cypripedi*]

Hosts This bacterial pathogen appears restricted to the orchid family and is known to be a serious disease on *Paphiopedilum* and *Cypripedium*, but less damaging on *Aerides, Catasetum, Phalaenopsis* and *Phragmipedium*.

Distribution Japan, Taiwan and the United States.

Symptoms This bacterium can become systemic within the host and therefore incurable. Disease is favored by temperatures between 80 and 88 F (26.5 and 31 C) but is still active at 98 F (37 C). The first symptoms of bacterial brown rot are small, round-to-oval, water-soaked spots, often located near the middle of the leaf. As the disease progresses, the color of the spot changes from a light brown to a very dark chestnut brown. The spot enlarges in all directions, finally reaching the growing point. Once in the growing point, it soon spreads throughout the plant, leaving it a dark-colored, shriveled, dried mass.

Management Use the management strategy presented under Bacterial Soft Rot. Additionally, if infection reaches the crown or stem, this organism can become systemic within the plant. These plants should be rogued and destroyed.

Fusarium Wilt [*Fusarium oxysporum and Fusarium oxysporum* f.sp. *cattleyae*]

Host *Aerides, Ascocenda, Brassavola, Brassocattleya, Brassolaeliocattleya, Bulbophyllum, Catasetum, Cattleya, Cycnoches, Cymbidium, Dendrobium, Epicattleya, Epidendrum, Eria, Grammatophyllum, Laelia, Laeliocattleya, Lycaste, Oncidium, Phalaenopsis, Potinara, Sophrolaeliocattleya* and *Vanda*. This fungus is specific to genera of the orchid family.

Distribution Reported from California, Florida, Missouri, New York, Ohio. It is probably nationwide.

Symptoms This disease was first described in 1961 from Ohio and later from Florida in 1964. The fungus may infect a plant through roots or by invading the plant through cut ends of rhizomes on plants recently divided. Severely infected plants may die three to nine weeks following infection. Generally, however, the plants live a year or longer in a state of continuing decline. The above-ground symptoms are similar to those caused by *Rhizoctonia solani*. The plants have yellow, thin, shriveled leaves and pseudobulbs that are somewhat twisted. Both diseases result in the rotting of roots. The diagnostic symptom of Fusarium wilt is found in the rhizome as a circle or band of purple discoloration in the epidermis and hypodermis with light pink vascular bundles (xylem and phloem). Eventually, the entire rhizome may be invaded and show purple discoloration. In some cases, the rot will extend an inch or so up the pseudobulb.

Management Where plants have previously died, heat-treat pots before reuse or dip in a dilution of household bleach in water (1:9) for 10 to 15 minutes. Rinse well before use. Physan dips can also be used according to the label. Osmunda is known to carry *Fusarium* spores and mycelium. Treat osmunda in a four percent formaldehyde drench and aerate several days before use. Formaldehyde is a toxic and offensive sterilant to use. Another option is the use of metam sodium (Vapam) as a drench fumigant under tarp. This product is a Restricted Use Pesticide and can be applied in a watering

Dormant survival structures (sclerotia) of *Sclerotium rolfsii*.

Crown decay caused by *Sclerotium rolfsii*.

can or through a hose-end sprayer. Keep tarp on for three to four days and aerate about two weeks (until odor is gone).

Inspect all stock for symptoms. Discard that part of the rhizome and pseudobulb showing infection. Plant only the part of the plant showing no purple discoloration. All diseased materials should be destroyed and general sanitation practices should be followed. Repot in new media with adequate drainage. Drench or dip sanitized plants in a thiophanate-methyl or iprodione-based fungicide.

Phyllosticta Stem Rot See Phyllosticta Leaf Spot under Leaf Spots

Rhizoctonia Root Rot [*Rhizoctonia solani*]

Host The broad pathogenicity of this soil fungus among plants would imply general susceptibility among genera and hybrids of orchids. Literature identifies this disease from *Aerides, Aliceara, Brassavola, Brassocattleya, Brassolaeliocattleya, Cattleya, Cymbidium, Dendrobium, Doritaenopsis, Epicattleya, Epidendrum, Laeliocattleya, Oncidium, Paphiopedilum, Phalaenopsis, Potinara, Sophrolaeliocattleya, Trichocentrum* and *Vanda*. The nonorchid host range for this fungus is one of the largest of known plant pathogenic fungi and includes agronomic crops, fruits, ornamentals, turfgrasses and vegetables.

Distribution Cosmopolitan.

Symptoms This disease may destroy susceptible orchids at any plant age. A damping-off disease is reported from *Cattleya, Oncidium, Paphiopedilum* and *Phalaenopsis* species and hybrids. Reports of mature-plant death from the previous orchids as well as *Rhyncholaelia digbyana, Brassavola nodosa, Trichocentrum alboviolaceum, Vanda, Cypripedium, Dendrobium* and *Epidendrum* are known. This fungus is primarily a brown, dry root-rot organism but may colonize the rhizomes, basal portion of the pseudobulb and even into lower seedling leaves. Disease progress is slow. Plants with root decay lose vigor, with leaves and pseudobulbs becoming yellow, shriveled, thin and twisted. New growth flushes are smaller. At this stage, plants thus affected are usually discarded by the grower. If this disease is unchecked, plant death can occur.

Management Avoid unsterile pots and media. Keep plants elevated beyond splash distance when over-seasoning out-of-doors. Early disease development can be partially managed by pruning of infected roots. Follow pruning with drench applications of thiophanate-methyl fungicides, iprodione or quintozene. Surface sprays of Captan will aid in damping-off occurrences.

Southern Blight [*Sclerotium rolfsii*]

Hosts *Cattleya, Cycnoches, Cymbidium, Dendrobium, Phaius tankervilleae* (syn. *Phaius grandifolius*), *Phalaenopsis, Spathoglottis plicata* and *Vanda.* This fungus has a broad host range outside the orchid family, including such hosts as peanut, bean, citrus, cucumber, tomato, banana, rice, potato and many ornamental crops and weed species.

Distribution Cosmopolitan throughout the tropical and warm temperate zones.

Symptoms The main symptom of this disease on orchids is a rapid collapse and rotting of the roots, pseudobulbs and lower parts of leaves. This rotting is characterized by a cream-yellow discoloration that soon turns brown because of subsequent invasion of tissue by secondary organisms. The formation of small, tan sclerotia on the affected tissue is a diagnostic characteristic of this fungus. (Sclerotia [plural], sclerotium [singular], meaning hardened mass of fungal threads in which food material is stored and which is capable of remaining dormant for long periods. The sclerotia are the size and color of mustard seeds. Sclerotia may persist in soil or in potting media for an indefinite period of time.

Management At first symptom development, remove plants carefully from the collection and destroy them. Treat pots before reuse as mentioned under Fusarium wilt (page 55). Do not reuse media. Drench surrounding plants with quintozene as a protectant. Remember to elevate plants beyond splash distance of the ground when moving plants out of doors during the summer.

Vanilla Root Rot [*Fusarium oxysporum* and *F. oxysporum* f. sp. *vanillae*]

Host Limited to *Vanilla.* This fungus is the most destructive pathogen on com-

Anthracnose on a cattleya with sexual structures of the Glomerella stage of this fungus.

mercial vanilla crops worldwide (*Vanilla planifolia*). Both *Vanilla barbellata* and *Vanilla pompona* are also susceptible, whereas *Vanilla phaeantha* is somewhat resistant to this fungus.

Symptoms The first symptoms are the browning and death of the roots. Because many vanilla roots are partly aerial, their death is easily noticed. The underground portion of the root usually becomes infected first. It turns dark brown and decays. The rot is either soft and watery or somewhat dry, depending on moisture conditions. Eventually, the aerial portions of the roots shrivel and die. As more and more roots die, the plant growth slows down as its energy is utilized for root regeneration. Root reestablishment may continue for a year or longer, but the plant eventually dies.

Management Follow the sanitation steps listed for management of Fusarium wilt (page 55). Procure only pathogen-

57

Bacterial brown spot caused by *Pseudomonas cattleyae* is the most common and severe disease of phalaenopsis. Diseased areas show a considerable amount of exudate, which contains infectious bacteria that may be carried to other plants by splashing water.

Bacterial brown spot caused by *Pseudomonas cattleyae* appears on *Cattleya*-like orchids as sunken black spots that are clearly delimited.

free cuttings for propagation. For existing disease, use of thiophanate methyl-based fungicides or iprodione will aid in disease control. Make several applications.

LEAF SPOTS

Anthracnose [*Colletotrichum gloeosporioides* (syn. *Gloeosporium affine* and *Gloeosporium cinctum*/*Glomerella cingulata*)] Research has demonstrated that American and European anthracnose diseases are caused by the same fungus.

Hosts *Aerides, Aliceara, Angraecum, Ansellia, Ascocenda, Ascocentrum, Brassavola, Brassia, Brassocattleya, Brassolaeliocattleya, Bulbophyllum, Catasetum, Cattleya, Cattleytonia, Cochleanthes, Cymbidium, Cyrtopodium, Dendrobium, Doritis, Epicattleya, Epidendrum, Eria, Gongora, Grammatophyllum, Huntleya, Ionopsis, Laelia, Laeliocattleya, Lockhartia, Lycaste, Maxillaria, Miltonia, Neomoorea, Odontocidium, Odontoglossum, Oncidium, Paphiopedilum, Peristeria, Pescatorea, Phaiocalanthe, Phaius, Phalaenopsis, Phragmipedium, Pleurothallis, Renades, Rhynchostylis, Rodriguezia, Schombodiacrium, Schomboepidendrum, Sophrolaeliocattleya, Spathoglottis, Stanhopea, Trichopilia, Vanda, Vandopsis, Vanilla, Vuylstekeara, Wilson-*

ara and *Zygopetalum*. Nonorchid hosts are many and include species important to agriculture and horticulture.

Distribution Worldwide with greater abundance in tropical and subtropical zones than in temperate ones.

Symptoms These organisms can attack any of the above-ground portions of the plant. Leaves are most often attacked, especially on plants that have been injured by cold, sun, chemicals or weakened due to poor root systems. The first symptom is a brown discoloration on leaves and pseudobulbs which is round or irregular in shape, more or less sunken, yellow to light green and rather sharply defined. As the disease progresses, fruiting bodies (asexual: acervuli, sexual: perithecia) develop in large numbers in the dead areas. When this happens, there is a distinct line of demarcation between the diseased and healthy tissue. On old or weakened flowers, small, round, brown to black spots develop on the sepals and petals. These spots may coalesce to cover a large part, if not all, of the blossom.

Management See *Cercospora dendrobii* under *Cercospora* Leaf Spots (page 60).

Bacterial Brown Spot [*Acidovorax cattleya* (syn. *Pseudomonas cattleya*)]

Hosts *Aerides, Ascocenda, Ascocentrum, Asconopsis, Brassia, Brassolaeliocattleya, Catasetum, Cattleya, Cymbi-*

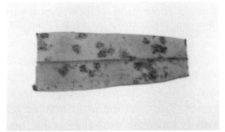

The underside of a leaf of *Angraecum Veitchii* marred by *Cercospora angraeci* leafspot.

Leafspot caused by *Cercospora dendrobii* on the top and bottom leaf surfaces of *Dendrobium nobile*. Soon after infection, a yellow-green area can be seen on the top surface of the leaf.

dium, Cyrtopodium, Dendrobium, Diaphananthe, Doritaenopsis, Epidendrum, Epiphronitis, Grammatophyllum, Hawaiiara, Ionopsis, Laeliocattleya, Miltonia, Odontocidium, Odontoglossum, Paphiopedilum, Phalaenopsis, Phragmipedium, Renantanda, Renanthera, Renanthopsis, Rhynchostylis, Rodricidium, Rodriguezia, Saccolabium, Sarcanthus, Sophrolaeliocattleya, Sophronitis, Stanhopea, Trichocidium, Vanda, Vandachnis, Vandopsis and *Vanilla.*

Distribution Europe, Queensland and the United States.

Symptoms The first symptom noted on phalaenopsis is a water-soaked lesion, which eventually becomes brown or black. The disease advances rapidly and, if not controlled, may result in the death of mature plants or seedlings in community pots. Infection may take place anywhere in the leaf, and, if it spreads to the crown, the plant is doomed. Diseased areas always show a considerable amount of exudate, which contains infectious bacteria that may be carried to other plants by splashing water. The disease appears on *Cattleya*-like orchids as sunken black spots which are clearly delimited.

Management Acquire only pathogen-free plants and isolate new stock for at least four weeks before integration with existing stock. At first disease incidence, sanitize infected plant parts. Water early

in the morning to encourage rapid drying. Reduce overhead irrigation frequency. Apply sprays of Physan or Captan as bactericides. Copper sulfate-based fungicides are also effective against bacteria but may be phytotoxic to orchid genera, especially plants in bloom or when temperatures exceed 90 F (32 C).

Bacterial Soft Rot See entry under Root, Stem and Pseudobulb Rots (page 53)

Brown Rot See entry under Root, Stem and Pseudobulb Rots (page 55)

Cercospora Leaf Spots
Cercospora Leaf Spot caused by *Cercospora angraeci*

Hosts *Angraceum* (*A. eburneum, A. sesquipedale, A. superbum, A.* Veitchii, *A.* Orchidglade), *Cattleya, Dendrobium, Jumellea* (syn. *Angraecum*) *comorensis, Jumellea* (syn. *Angraecum*) *fragrans, Macroplectrum* and *Odontoglossum.*

Distribution France, Great Britain, Malaysia and the United States (Florida).

Symptoms Infection first starts on *Angraecum* Veitchii as a yellow spot on the undersurface of the leaves. The spot enlarges in an irregular pattern, becomes sunken and turns purplish brown to purplish black in color. The corresponding top leaf surface first becomes chlorotic and finally necrotic.

59

Phaius tankervilleae exhibiting symptoms of leafspot caused by *Cercospora epipactidis*. Tiny sunken yellow spots on the underside of the leaf eventually become visible on both surfaces, darken and may coalesce into large irregular lesions. With age, the centers of the spots may fall out.

Management See *Cercospora dendrobii* (below).

Cercospora Leaf Spot caused by *Cercospora dendrobii*

Hosts Only species and hybrids of *Dendrobium*. Both deciduous and evergreen *Dendrobium* types are susceptible.

Distribution Southeastern United States (described first in Florida) and Japan.

Symptoms The first symptoms are noted on the underside of the leaves as light yellow spots. The spots continue to enlarge in a circular or regular pattern and may eventually engulf the whole leaf. With age, the spots become slightly sunken and purple-black with the advancing margin remaining yellow. Soon after infection takes place a corresponding yellow-green area can be noted on the top surface of the leaf. Old spots are purplish black and may somewhat resemble spider mite damage. Heavily infected leaves usually fall from the plant prematurely. This is especially true if infection takes place near the base of the leaf.

Management Fungal leaf diseases are generally cosmetic rather than serious. All control efforts must bear in mind that once a leaf is infected, the lesion cannot be reversed. Isolate infected plants and reduce leaf wetness to slow disease spread. All control strategies begin with the sanitation of infected tissue. This improves plant appearance, reduces fungal reproduction and eradicates the fungus from the plant since the pathogen is localized in the leaf spot. When leaf spot incidence becomes severe, use of fungicides may be needed. The only systemic fungicide available for widespread use on orchids contains thiophanate methyl. Alternative protectant fungicides include mancozeb and ferbam.

Use of thiophanate methyl-based fungicides should be limited to two applications unless either alternated or tank-mixed with a protectant product.

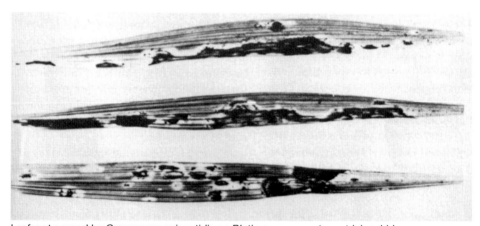

Leafspot caused by *Cercospora epipactidis* on *Bletia purpurea*, a terrestrial orchid.

Cattleya-like orchids in community pots can exhibit leafspot caused by *Cercospora odontoglossi* on the underside of leaves. Initially, tiny, slightly raised, dark brown spots are evident.

On older seedlings and mature cattleya-like orchids, leafspot caused by *Cercospora odontoglossi* turns the bottom surface of the leaf purplish black.

Cercospora Leaf Spot caused by *Cercospora epipactidis*

Hosts *Anguloa, Ansellia, Bletia, Brassia, Calanthe, Catasetum, Chysis, Coelogyne, Cycnoches, Cyrtopodium, Dendrochilum, Epidendrum, Eulophia, Gongora, Lycaste, Maxillaria, Mendoncella, Monomeria, Neomoorea, Pescatorea, Phaius, Phaiocalanthe, Spathoglottis, Stanhopea, Xylobium* and *Zygopetalum.*

Distribution Italy, Germany and Russia on *Epipactis latifolia* and *Epipactis polustrus.* Also reported from the United States (Florida, Louisiana, Massachusetts, New York, South Carolina, Tennessee, Washington and Wyoming) and Mexico.

Symptoms The first symptoms on *Phaius tankervilleae* appear as tiny, sunken, yellow spots on the undersurface of the leaves. As the disease advances, the spotting is visible on both leaf surfaces. The spots continue to enlarge until they are about ¹/₄ inch (6 mm) or more in diameter. They are sunken and purplish-black in color, with a raised margin of a slightly darker color. Some of the spots may coalesce to form large irregular lesions. With age, the centers of the spots fall out.

Management See *Cercospora dendrobii* (above). Always precede fungicide selection and use by a rigorous sanitation of infected plant parts to improve fungicide performance.

Cercospora Leaf Spot caused by *Cercospora odontoglossi*

Hosts *Ascocenda, Brassavola, Brassocattleya, Brassolaelia, Brassolaeliocattleya, Broughtonia, Cattleya, Caularthron, Dendrobium, Epicattleya, Epidendrum, Epilaeliocattleya, Epitonia, Laelia, Laeliocattleya, Laelonia, Pleurothallis, Potinara, Rodricidium, Rodriguezia, Schombocattleya, Schombodiacrium, Sophrolaelia, Sophrolaeliocattleya* and *Sophronitis.*

Distribution Brazil, France, New Zealand, the United States (California, Florida, Louisiana, Maryland, Massachusetts) and Venezuela.

Symptoms Symptoms are first noted on the undersides of leaves on seedlings in community pots as tiny, slightly raised, dark brown spots. The fungus usually spreads rapidly, eventually engulfing the entire leaf. When this happens the leaf dies. The corresponding top leaf surface becomes chlorotic and finally necrotic. Often all the leaves on small seedlings become infected, and the plant dies. Occasionally, a heavily infected seedling will still have enough vitality to put out new growth. If not protected by a fungicide, it too may die.

The first symptoms on older seedlings and mature plants begin as slightly sunken, yellow, round to irregular areas on the undersides of leaves. With age,

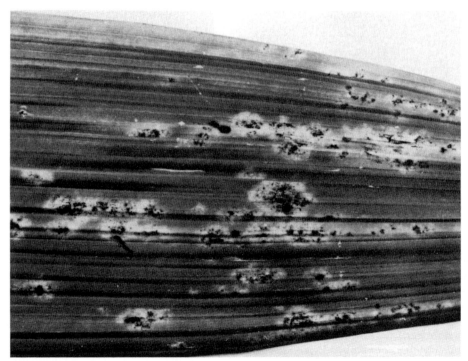

Peristeria elata, commonly called the dove orchid, is the only known host for leafspot caused by *Cercospora peristeriae*. Spores of this fungus are produced almost entirely on the undersides of the leaves.

they turn purplish black in color. The corresponding top surface of the leaf is chlorotic but eventually becomes necrotic.

Seedlings in community pots and plants in 2-inch (5-cm) pots have been killed by this fungus. Plants of any age are susceptible, but the disease is not as destructive to large seedlings or mature plants. It does, however, leave unsightly spots that remain during the life of the leaf on older plants.

Cercospora Leaf Spot caused by *Cercospora peristeriae*

Host *Peristeria elata.*

Distribution Florida.

Symptoms The disease is noted first on the underside of the leaf as yellowish to pale brown, oval to elongate spots. Within a few days, infection spreads to both leaf surfaces. As the disease pro-

gresses, the spots enlarge to $^3/_{16}$ to 2 inches (.5 to 5 cm) in diameter and become tan with a purple border. Spores of this fungus are produced almost entirely on the undersides of the leaves.

Management See *Cercospora dendrobii* (page 60).

Cercospora Leaf Spot caused by *Cercospora* species

Host *Cattleya*-like orchids.

Distribution Alabama, Florida, Georgia, Louisiana, Ohio, South Carolina, Virginia and Wisconsin.

Symptoms The symptoms expressed by this fungus are different from those produced by *Cercospora odontoglossi.* The latter usually causes rather large, circular to irregular spots on the lower surface of mature *Cattleya*-like orchids whereas the former usually causes uni-

Leafspot caused by *Cercospora* sp. on top and bottom of leaves of a cattleya-like orchid. Unlike leafspot induced by *Cercospora odontoglossi*, this fungus usually causes uniform tiny spots on the lower surface of the leaves.

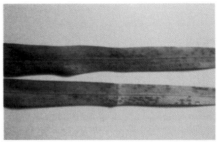

Leaves of a hybrid cymbidium exhibiting damage from leafspot caused by *Cercospora* species. The disease is more severe on older foliage.

form tiny spots on the lower surface of the leaves. Symptoms show as tiny, slightly sunken, purple-brown spots, usually a millimeter or less in diameter, on the undersides of leaves. It is not unusual to find entire leaves invaded by this fungus, causing thousands of discrete, tiny spots that weaken the leaves and cause them to fall prematurely. The corresponding upper leaf surface is a light yellow-green color. The oldest leaves are usually most severely infected, but leaves not fully mature also may be attacked.

Management See *Cercospora dendrobii* (page 60). Always precede fungicide use

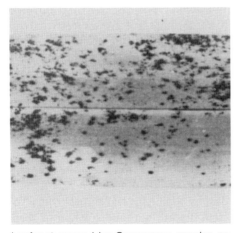

Leafspot caused by *Cercospora* species on the underside of leaf of an oncidium.

by rigorous sanitation of infected plant parts to improve disease control.

Cercospora Leaf Spot caused by *Cercospora* species

Hosts *Cymbidium, Cymbidiella* and *Grammatophyllum* spp.

Distribution Florida, Georgia, Kentucky, Louisiana, South Carolina and Tennessee.

Symptoms Tiny spots are on the underside of leaves. They are round, slightly sunken, dark brown, and usually less than $\frac{1}{16}$ inch (less than 1 mm) in diameter. Several spots may coalesce to form a larger spot. The corresponding upper leaf surface will first exhibit a yellow-green spot but later may turn brown with a slight yellow halo. The disease is more severe on older leaves.

Management See *Cercospora dendrobii* (page 60).

Cercospora Leaf Spot caused by *Cercospora* species

Hosts *Comparettia, Miltonia, Oncidium, Rodrettia, Rodricidium* and *Rodriguezia*.

Distribution Florida, Georgia, Louisiana and South Carolina.

Symptoms Tiny spots are found on the undersurface of leaves. Individual spots are usually less than $\frac{1}{16}$ inch (less than 1 mm) in diameter, sunken, reddish purple, with a slightly raised light tan center.

Leafspot caused by *Cercospora* species on a vanda.

With age, the entire spot becomes sunken. When two or more spots coalesce, they eventually become sunken, reddish purple, and several millimeters across. The upper leaf surface is light green.

Management See *Cercospora dendrobii* (page 60).

Cercospora Leaf Spot caused by *Cercospora* species

Hosts *Aerides, Aeridovanda, Arachnis, Ascocenda, Ascocentrum, Doritis, Phalaenopsis, Renanthera, Rhynchostylis* and *Vanda*.

Distribution Florida.

Symptoms Symptoms show on the undersides of leaves as tiny sunken spots, usually $\frac{1}{16}$ inch (1 mm) or less in diameter, that are purple-brown. Spots may coalesce to form a larger spot. The upper leaf surface is yellow-green in color and with age may become purple-brown.

Management See *Cercospora dendrobii* (page 60).

Diplodia Leaf Spot [*Diplodia laeliocattleyae* and *Diplodia* spp.]

Hosts *Cattleya, Brassolaeliocattleya, Laeliocattleya* and other hybrids. Unspeciated *Diplodia* fungi are reported to cause a stem rot on *Ansellia* and leaf spots on *Epidendrum, Laelia, Pleurothallis* and *Stanhopea*.

Distribution Florida and Europe.

Symptoms Infection begins as small, yellow spots on either leaf surface. The spots continue to enlarge, turn brown and eventually appear as black, greasy lesions. The fruiting structures of the fungus (pycnidia) are black, raised and develop in the older spots.

Management This disease is usually minor in importance and often associated with weakened or stressed leaves. Sanitize affected plants of diseased tissue. If severity warrants, use of a mancozeb fungicide will be helpful as a foliar spray.

Flyspeck [*Schizothyrium perexiguum* (syn. *Microthyriella rubi*) and *Leptothyrium* spp.]

Hosts *Brassocattleya, Brassolaeliocattleya, Broughtonia, Cattleya, Dendrobium, Epidendrum, Laeliocattleya, Miltonia, Oncidium, Rodriguezia, Sophrolaeliocattleya* and *Vanda*.

Distribution United States.

Symptoms Although this fungus is widespread, it causes little damage, and unless one looks closely, it easily escapes detection. Flyspeck often is accompanied by another fungus, *Gloeodes pomigena*, that produces a superficial black film on leaves called sooty blotch (see sooty blotch below). Tiny black specks consisting of closely woven hyphae of the fungus, about the size and color of a flyspeck, can occur on either leaf surface. Individual spots are slightly elevated, black, definite and grow superficially on the leaf. Spots usually occur in groups of six to 50 or more. Although each speck seems to be independent of the others, closer examination shows that a very fine thread of the fungus connects them.

Management This disease is such a minor problem that control options are normally not needed. Increase lighting conditions to disfavor the fungus. Buildup of this fungus can best be handled by wiping the leaf surface with a soft cloth dipped in a mild solution of soapy water. Use of mancozeb fungicides will aid in disease management if needed.

Leaves of a vanda displaying symptoms of leafspot caused by *Guignardia* species.

Leafspot caused by *Phyllostictina capitalensis* is generally not a serious disease of orchids, but because of the unsightly spotting of the leaves, it can detract from a plant's appearance. It affects species and hybrids in many genera, including the *Dendrobium thyrsiflorum*, shown here.

Guignardia Leaf Spot caused by *Guignardia* species

Hosts *Ascocenda, Ascocentrum, Brassocattleya, Brassolaeliocattleya, Laeliocattleya, Phaius, Rhynchostylis* and *Vanda*.

Distribution Southeastern United States.

Symptoms Initial infection may start on either side of a leaf as tiny, dark purple, elongated lesions. These lesions run parallel to the direction of the veins but are not delimited by the veins. The lesions elongate into purple streaks or diamond-shaped areas. The individual lesions often coalesce to form irregular areas that may engulf a large part of the leaf. With age, the center of the lesion turns tan, and raised, black fruiting structures of the fungus develop.

Management This disease can develop to serious levels on select susceptible genera of orchids. Sanitize infected foliage and manage irrigation to wet foliage infrequently and timed to encourage rapid leaf drying. Use of either Captan, ferbam, mancozeb or thiophanate-methyl-based fungicides will aid in disease control. Repeat applications will be needed.

Phyllosticta Leaf Spot [*Phyllosticta capitalensis* (syn. *Phyllostictina pyriformis*)]

Hosts *Aerides, Angraecum, Anota, Arachnis, Ascocenda, Ascocentrum, Aspasia, Beallara, Bifrenaria, Brassavola, Brassia, Brassocattleya, Brassolaeliocattleya, Brassotonia, Broughtonia, Catasetum, Cattleya, (Cattleya-like orchids), Cattleytonia, Caularthron, Chondrorhyncha, Cochleanthes, Cymbidiella, Cymbidium, Cyrtopodium, Cyrtorchis, Dendrobium, Encyclia, Epicattleya, Epidendrum, Eulophiella, Gongora, Grammatophyllum, Haemaria, Huntleya, Isochilus, Laelia, Laeliopsis, Laeliocattleya, Lockhartia, Masdevallia, Maxillaria, Miltonia, Miltonidium, Odontocidium, Odontoglossum, Odontonia, Oncidium, Opsistylis, Paphiopedilum, Pescatorea, Phalaenopsis, Pleurothallis, Renancentrum, Renanthera, Renanthopsis, Rhynchostylis, Rhynchovanda, Rodricidium, Schombocattleya, Scuticaria, Sophrolaeliocattleya, Spathoglottis, Stanhopea, Stelis, Trichopilia, Trigonidium, Vanda, Vandachnis, Vandopsis, Vanilla, Vuylstekeara, Xylobium* and *Zygopetalum*.

Distribution This disease of orchids is known to occur in Australia, Aruba, the Netherlands Antilles, The British Virgin Islands, the Canal Zone, Costa Rica, Grand Cayman Island, Haiti, Honduras,

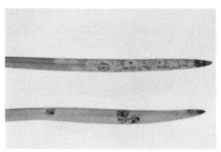

The rust *Sphenospora kevorkianii* on the underside of leaves of *Encyclia tampensis*.

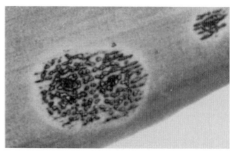

The rust *Sphenospora kevorkianii* on the underside of leaves of *Epicattleya* Acutiepie.

India, Jamaica, Japan, Mexico, the Philippines, Thailand, Trinidad, Venezuela and in the United States (California, Colorado, Florida, Georgia, Indiana, Kentucky, Louisiana, Massachusetts, New York, Ohio, Pennsylvania, South Carolina, Tennessee, Texas, Virginia, Washington and Wyoming).

Symptoms This leafspot is generally not a serious disease of orchids, but because of the unsightly spotting of the leaves, it detracts from the plant's appearance. Some dendrobiums often are severely spotted due to this fungus, which can result in premature defoliation. Spots may start anywhere on a leaf or pseudobulb as tiny, slightly sunken, yellow lesions. As they continue to enlarge, they become round to oval, sunken, especially if the infection is on the leaves, turning tan to dark brown with a slightly raised, red to purple-black margin. The tan or brown center of the spots develops tiny, black, raised structures (pycnidia) which contain the spores of the fungus. The average spot is about 1/4 inch (6 mm) in diameter but some may be larger or smaller.

Management See *Cercospora dendrobii* (page 60).

Rust caused by *Coleosporium bletiae*

Hosts *Phaius*, specifically *P. mishmensis*, *P. tankervilleae* and *P. wallichii*.

Distribution Florida, eastern Asia and India.

Symptoms This disease is recognized by the orange rust pustules found on both leaf surfaces and also on the flower stalks. Early infection starts as tiny yellow spots on either side of the leaf. Within a few days, orange spore masses develop. As the spots continue to enlarge in a circular pattern, the outside margin is orange, due to the spore masses, while the center turns brown and often falls out. A yellow halo is noticeable around the periphery of the spots. Individual lesions are usually less than 1/2 inch (12 mm) in diameter. Lesions on the flower stalks are often larger than those on the leaves. They are oval, with a halo around the outside of the spot.

Management Rust fungi can be characterized by possessing high reproductive rates. At the first sign of disease, infected plants should be isolated in space downwind from other plants. Sanitize as much infected tissue as possible and apply either ferbam or mancozeb fungicides as needed according to the label.

Rust caused by *Sphenospora kevorkianii/Uredo nigropuncto*

Hosts This rust attacks a wide array of orchid genera. Those reported are *Batemannia, Bletia, Brassia, Bulbophyllum, Capanemia, Catasetum, Cattleya,*

Caularthron, Cycnoches, Cyrtopodium, Encyclia, Epicattleya, Epidendrum, Gongora, Hexisea, Huntleya, Ionopsis, Laelia, Leochilus, Lockhartia, Lycaste, Masdevallia, Maxillaria, Miltonia, Mormodes, Notylia, Odontoglossum, Oeceoclades, Oncidium, Pelexia, Peristeria, Pescatorea, Ornithocephalus, Pleurothallis, Polystachya, Rodriguezia, Sigmatostalix, Stanhopea, Trichoceros, Trichopilia, Trigonidium, Xylobium, Zygopetalum and *Zygostates*.

Distribution This rust fungus has been found attacking orchids in the following countries: The Bahamas, Belize, Brazil, Bolivia, Colombia, Costa Rica, the Dominican Republic, Ecuador, El Salvador, Guadalupe, Guatemala, Honduras, Jamaica, Mexico, Nicaragua, Panama, Peru, Haiti, Surinam, Trinidad and Tobago, Venezuela, the United States (Florida) and the West Indies.

Symptoms On *Encyclia tampensis*, the symptoms first appear as small, orange spore pustules on the leaf undersurface. As the lesion enlarges, the orange pustules eventually rupture the top surface of the leaf. The pustules turn black with age. They often develop in a concentric pattern, which gives the infected area the appearance of a target spot. Only the leaf area is attacked by this fungus.

Management See *Coleosporium bletiae* (page 66). Because this rust has such a wide orchid host range, it may be advisable to rogue and destroy infected plants.

Rust caused by *Sphenospora mera*

Hosts This rust fungus is reported to infect *Bletia, Bletilla, Catasetum, Cycnoches, Epidendrum, Ionopsis, Mormodes, Oncidium, Pleurothallis* and *Rodriguezia*.

Distribution Documented from Brazil, Costa Rica, Dominican Republic, El Salvador, Honduras, Mexico, Peru, the

Sphenospora mera, a rust on the underside of a leaf of *Epidendrum nocturnum*. Spores of the rust can be spread to other orchids by wind or splashing water. This fungus infects leaves only.

United States (Florida) and Venezuela.

Symptoms On *Cycnoches chlorochilon*, the disease starts on the undersurface of leaves, as tiny, raised, cinnamon-brown spots. When the spots become mature, they rupture and cinnamon-to-golden-brown powdery spore masses are produced. Individual spores may be carried by wind or splashing water, often infecting nearby susceptible orchids. Only the leaves are infected by this fungus.

Management See *Coleosporium bletiae* (page 66). If orchid collections reflect high numbers of susceptible plants, diseased plants might best be rogued and destroyed rather than risk disease spread. Rust spores are produced in high numbers on infected leaves and are easily moved by air and water.

Rust caused by *Sphenospora saphena*

Hosts Known susceptible orchid genera include *Cochlioda, Epidendrum, Ionopsis, Laelia, Masdevallia, Oncidium, Pescatorea, Rodriguezia* and *Sobralia*.

Distribution This disease has been reported from the following countries: The Bahamas, Belize, Brazil, Colombia, Costa Rica, the Dominican Republic, Ecuador, Guatemala, Honduras, Haiti, Jamaica, Mexico, Peru, Surinam, Trinidad and Tobago, Venezuela and the United States (Florida).

Symptoms On *Oncidium tetrapetalum*, this rust is found on the undersurface of the leaves as tiny, raised orange or rust brown pustules. When infection is severe, the underside of the leaves literally may be covered with these spore-bearing pustules. As the pustules become older, they turn dark brown.

Management See *Coleosporium bletiae* (page 65). If orchid collections reflect high numbers of susceptible plants, destroy diseased plants rather than risk airborne fungal spore spread.

The rust *Uredo behnickiana* on the underside of a leaf of *Laelia anceps*. Even severely infected plants may bloom, but the inflorescences are smaller than normal, with fewer and smaller flowers.

Rust caused by *Uredo behnickiana*

Hosts *Brassavola, Catasetum, Cattleya dowiana, Cattleya dowiana* var. *aurea, Cattleya guttata, Bletia purpurea, Dendrobium* spp., *Encyclia alata, Hexisea* spp., *Laelia anceps, Laelia aurea, Laelia autumnalis, Laelia undulata, Masdevallia* spp., *Maxillaria* spp., *Prosthechea* (syn. *Encyclia*) *mariae, Prosthechea* (syn. *Encyclia*) *vitellina, Oncidium crispum, Oncidium dasytyle, Oncidium marshallianum, Oncidium varicosum, Phaius tankervilleae, Pleurothallis* spp., *Sophronitis* (syn. *Laelia*) *pumila, Spathoglottis plicata, Stanhopea* spp., *Tolumnia guttata* (syn. *Oncidium guttatum*) and *Trichocentrum* (syn. *Oncidium*) *cavendishianum*.

Distribution Areas where this rust fungus has been found attacking orchids are: Bolivia, Brazil, Costa Rica, Cuba, Dominican Republic, Ecuador, Guatemala, Honduras, Jamaica, Mexico, Nicaragua, Puerto Rico and the United States (Florida, New Jersey, Ohio).

Symptoms This disease was found in Florida in 1954 on *Phaius tankervilleae* (syn. *P. grandifolius*) imported from Cuba. Many of the infected plants died or became so unthrifty that they were discarded. On *P. tankervilleae*, the rust is on the underside of the leaves as orange-yellow patches. The patches enlarge in a more or less circular pattern and eventually may cover the entire lower surface of the leaves. The top surface of the leaves directly over the patches becomes chlorotic. Even severely infected plants may bloom, but the inflorescences are smaller, with fewer and smaller flowers. Only the leaves are attacked.

Management See rust caused by *Sphenospora saphena* (page 67).

Rust caused by *Uredo epidendri*

Hosts The known hosts are *Caularthron bilamellatum, Epidendrum nocturnum, Ionopsis* spp., *Laelia* spp., *Prosthechea pastoris* (syn. *Encyclia venosa*), *Rodriguezia* spp. and *Trichocentrum* (syn. *Oncidium*) *cavendishianum*.

Distribution Tropical regions and the United States (Florida).

Symptoms The first symptoms are noted on the undersides of leaves as raised brown pustules, often with reddish borders. As the disease progresses, both the upper and lower epidermis of the leaves are ruptured by the developing spore pustules. With age, the pustules change from brown to purple-black. Only the leaves are infected by this rust.

Management See rust caused by *Coleosporium bletiae* (page 66).

Leafspot caused by *Septoria selenophomoides* on a dendrobium. Species and hybrids of *Dendrobium nobile* are especially susceptible.

Rust caused by *Uredo oncidii*

Hosts *Oncidium* spp. Reports of this pathogen on *Epidendrum, Lycaste* and *Odontoglossum* spp. are tentative.

Distribution This rust has been found infecting orchids in Brazil, Colombia, Costa Rica, Ecuador, Guatemala, Mexico, Trinidad, Tobago and the United States (Florida, Hawaii, California).

Symptoms This disease is found on the undersurface of the leaves as small orange pustules. The orange, powdery material is the spore mass of the fungus. The infected area is usually circular. With age, the center turns brown, while the advancing outside margin is orange.

Management See rust caused by *Coleosporium bletiae* (page 66).

Septoria Leaf Spot [*Septoria selenophomoides*]

Hosts *Septoria selenophomoides* has been found on the following orchids imported into the United States: *Brassia verrucosa, Bulbophyllum napellii, Coelogyne cristata, Coelogyne stricta, Cuitlauzina pendula* (syn. *Odontoglossum citrosmum*), *Cymbidium aloifolium* (syn. *pendulum*), *Cymbidium devonianum, Cymbidium whiteae, Dendrobium bigibbum, Dendrobium forbesii* var. *forbesii* (syn. *ashworthiae*), *Dendrobium nobile, Dendrobium sarmentosum* (syn. *fragrans*), *Dendrobium schroederianum, Masdevallia ignea, Miltonia cuneata*

(syn. *Oncidium speciosum*), *Miltonia regnellii, Oncidium varicosum* var. *rogersii, Oncidium wentworthianum, Paphiopedilum insigne*, other *Paphiopedilum* spp., *Phalaenopsis* spp., *Pleurothallis* spp., *Prosthechea* (syn. *Cattleya*) *citrina, Prosthechea* (syn. *Encyclia*) *cochleata, Rhynchostele* (syn. *Odontoglossum*) *bictoniensis, Rhynchostele* (syn. *Odontoglossum*) *cordata, Rhynchostele* (syn. *Odontoglossum*) *uroskinneri, Sophronitis* (syn. *Laelia*) *tenebrosa, Stanhopea* spp. and *Stenocoryne*. Series and hybrids of *Dendrobium nobile* are especially susceptible.

Distribution This fungus on orchids has been reported from Brazil, Colombia, Dominican Republic, England, Guatemala, India, Japan, Great Britain, Mexico, Thailand, Costa Rica, the Philippines and the United States (Florida).

Symptoms On *Dendrobium nobile*, the spots may start on either leaf surface as tiny, sunken, yellow lesions. They continue to enlarge into circular or irregular patches on the leaf. Heavily infected leaves fall prematurely.

Management See Anthracnose under Leaf Spots (page 58).

Sooty Blotch [*Gloeodes pomigena*]

Hosts *Brassocattleya, Cattleya, Dendrobium, Epidendrum, Vanda* and other *Cattleya*-like orchids and hybrids. Nonorchid hosts include *Acer, Cercis, Citrus, Cornus, Crataegus, Fraxinus, Gaultheria, Lindera, Liriodendron, Magnolia, Malus, Platanus, Prunus, Pyrus, Quercus, Rhus, Rubus, Salix, Sassafras, Smilax, Sorbus, Ulmus, Vitis* and other woody species.

Distribution Temperate northern hemisphere.

Symptoms Sooty blotch is a name that adequately describes the general appearance of this fungus on orchid leaves. The spots are indefinite in outline and are gray to dull black in color. Individual blotches may be round, oval or irregular in shape and generally are between ½ and 1 inch (1.2 and 2.5 cm) in diameter. Often two or more blotches coalesce to form a large irregular area.

Management Sooty blotch is of minor importance to orchid growers. While common, it does only slight damage. It forms a sooty coating that grows superficially on pseudobulbs or on either side of the leaves. Because of the superficial growth, it easily can be removed by rubbing the affected areas with a damp cloth. Common orchid fungicides are effective but not required for this problem.

FLOWER BLIGHTS

Anthracnose See entry under Leaf Spots

Botrytis Petal Blight [*Botrytis cinerea*]
Hosts *Aerides, Ascocentrum, Brassia, Brassocattleya, Brassolaeliocattleya, Broughtonia, Calanthe, Cattleya, Cycnoches, Cymbidium, Dendrobium, Doritaenopsis, Epidendrum, Laelia, Laeliocattleya, Maxillaria, Miltonia, Oncidium, Paphiopedilum, Phaius, Phalaenopsis, Potinara, Trichoglottis, Vanda* and *Vanilla.* Nonorchid hosts of Botrytis are quite numerous as this fungus is a serious fruit- and flower-blight pathogen.

Distribution Cosmopolitan.

Symptoms Disease begins with small circular lesions on petals or sepals. These spots enlarge slightly and appear brown in color, often with a delicate pink margin. The fungus requires wet tissue or relative humidity greater than 92 to 93 percent for infection, preferring temperatures between 68 and 72 F (20 and 22 C). The fungus is also an aggressive invader of dead or dying flower or leaf tissue.

Management Inspect production space to minimize conditions favorable for

Petal blight caused by *Botrytis cinerea* is most common during cool, damp weather where there is inadequate air circulation. Although phalaenopsis (above) and cattleya-like flowers are most susceptible, other genera, including *Vanda, Oncidium* and *Dendrobium*, are subject to infection.

Botrytis development. Water early in the day to allow all foliage and flowers to dry off most rapidly. Use heat or forced air to reduce relative humidity below 92 percent. Sanitize infested tissue and all dead blooms to reduce reproduction of the fungus. Apply thiophanate methyl, iprodione, vinclozolin or Physan as needed.

Rust caused by *Coleosporium bletiae*
See entry under Leaf Spots (page 66)

Rust caused by *Uredo behnickiana* See entry under Leaf Spots (page 69)

Yellow Bud Blight [*Aphelenchoidis ritzema-bosi*]
Hosts Foliar nematode has been reported from *Vanda* Miss Joaquim. The pathogen is commonly reported from a diverse host range that may exceed 190 plant species, including chrysanthemum, gloxinia, *Saintpaulia*, peperomia, strawberry and others.

Distribution Reported on *Vanda* from Hawaii. This pathogen is known from the United States, Brazil, Europe, Russia and the former Sovet Republics, South Africa, New Zealand, Fiji, and elsewhere.

Symptoms The most diagnostic symptom appears on the unopened buds. Infected buds turn yellow, then brown, and usually shrivel and drop off. Heavily infected inflorescences become blackened, shriveled, and cease to set new flowers. After a period of time, these spikes die back. Moderately infected spikes show symptoms of russeting but quite often bear healthy flowers interspaced among the blighted buds.

Management Avoid orchid production that follows or is interspersed with other susceptible hosts to foliar nematode. Remove infected spikes and destroy these by burning. Infected plants can be hot-water treated by immersion in water at 115 F (46 C) for 10 minutes.

Legal Fungicides and Usage Information for Orchids

This information is compiled from available federal pesticide labels. Use of a trade name is solely for providing information and is not a guarantee or warranty of the products named, and does not signify approval to the exlusion of other products of suitable composition. Listing of a specific product does not ensure or guarantee absolute performance against a particular disease. Remember, the name of the crop to be treated must appear on the label. Diseases listed in this chapter to be treated by specific products may not always appear on the product label, as per flexibility provided by amended Federal Insecticide, Fungicide, and Rodenticide Act (FIFRA) legislation in 1996 [Section 2(ee)].

Captan (cis-N-trichloromethylthio-4-cyclohexene-1,2-dicarboximide)
Trade name: Captan 50 WP, Captan 80 WP.
Manufactured by Zeneca, Inc. Product cleared for use in both the field and greenhouse to control damping-off diseases as a protectant.
Legal usage: For use across ornamental plant species (seedling or transplant stage) grown in soil or greenhouse benches.
Comments: Apply as a directed soil surface spray.

Copper Sulfate, Basic (copper sulfate - $CuSO_4.3H_2O$)
Trade name: Cuproxat 27.1% F.

Manufactured by Agrolinz, Inc. Product cleared for outside (field) use only, not in an enclosed greenhouse. Used to protect leaves and stems from bacterial and fungal blights and spots.
Legal usage: Broadly legal across ornamentals.
Comments: Avoid use when air temperatures exceed 90 F (32 C) Do not apply to plants in bloom.

Etridiazole (5-Ethoxy-3-trichloromethyl-1,2,4-thiadiazole)
Trade names: Terrazole 35 WP and Truban 30 WP.
Manufactured by Uniroyal Chemicals Co. Inc. and Scotts Sierra Crop Protection Co., respectively. Product cleared for both greenhouse and outside use to control damping-off, stem and root diseases caused by *Phytophthora* and *Pythium* spp. as a protectant drench fungicide.
Legal usage: For use on *Cymbidium* spp. only.
Comments: Wash foliage free of residue after drench application.

Ferbam (Ferric dimethyldithiocarbamate)
Trade name: Carbamate 75% WDG.
Manufactured by FMC Agricultural Corp. Cleared for use outside only to control rust fungi as a protectant spray or damping-off diseases by soil-directed spray.
Legal usage: For use on orchids and generally on flowers.
Comments: Results in a conspicuous residue on plants.

Fosetyl Aluminum [Aluminum tris (-0-ethyl phosphonate)]
Trade name: Aliette 80% WP and WDG.
Manufactured by Rhone-Poulenc Inc. Product cleared for both greenhouse and outside use to control damping-off and root/stem rot diseases caused by *Phytophthora* and *Pythium* spp. as a systemic, curative spray or drench.
Legal usage: Broad legal use across flowers and ornamental plants at all growth stages. Specifically cleared on *Cattleya skinneri*.
Comments: Can affect root-disease control by a foliar spray as the active ingredient moves upward and downward within the plant. Do not spray within 7 days of copper fungicide use. Never tank-mix product with mancozeb fungicides, soluble fertilizer, spreader stickers, extenders or wetting agents. Liability for product use assumed by user as "orchids" are not specifically listed on the product label.

Iprodione {(3-,5-dichlorophenyl)-N-(1-methylethyl)-2,4-dioxo-1-imidazoli-dinecarboxamide)}
Trade name: Chipco 26019 WP(50%)
Manufactured by: Rhone-Poulenc Ag. Company. Product cleared for use in both greenhouse and field to control various foliar dieases caused by *Alternaria* spp., *Ascochyta* sp., *Botrytis* spp., *Drechslera* sp., *Fusarium moniliforme*, *Helminthosporium* spp., *Rhizoctonia* sp. and *Stagonospora*. Also used as a drench to control root/corm rots caused by *Rhizoctonia* spp. and *Fusarium oxysporum*.
Legal usage: Cleared for use on specific ornamentals as well as general clearance for use across ornamentals *providing* growers evaluate first for plant safety on a small scale.

Comments: Liability for product use assumed by the user as "orchids" are not specifically listed on the product label.

Mancozeb (Coordination product of zinc ion and manganese ethylene bisdithiocarbamate)
Trade names: Dithane T/O DF (75%), Dithane T/O F (37%), and Fore WP (80%).
Manufactured by Rohm & Haas Co. Product cleared for both greenhouse and outside use to control various leaf- and stem-spotting fungi as well as rust diseases as a protectant spray.
Legal usage: Broad legal use across ornamentals.
Comments: Performance may be improved by use of surfactant Latron B-1956. Liability for product use assumed by user as orchids are not specifically listed on the product labels.

Metalaxyl [N-(2,6-Dimethylphenyl)-N-(methoxyacetyl)-alanine methyl ester]
Trade name: Subdue 2E (21%), Subdue G (2%).
Manufactured by Ciba Plant Protection. Product cleared for use in both greenhouse and outside as a systemic drench fungicide to control damping-off, stem rots and root rots caused by *Phytophthora* and *Pythium* spp.

Legal usage: Broad legal use across flowers and ornamental plants
Comments: Strongly curative product. Liability for orchid use assumed by user as this plant family is not listed on the label.

(N-alkyl Dimethyl Benzyl and Ethyl Benzyl Ammonium Chlorides)
Trade name: Consan 20, Physan 20 and Green Shield.
Manufactured by Voluntary Purchasing Group, Maril Products, Inc. and Whitmire Research Laboratories, Inc. Product cleared for use in greenhouses to control algae, *Botrytis* flower blight, damping-off and *Erwinia* brown rot diseases as a contact pesticide.
Legal usage: For use on *Cymbidium* spp. and other orchids.
Comments: For cleansing work area, bench tops, pots, flats and cutting tools. Some efficacy against odontoglossum ringspot virus on work or cutting surfaces.

Quintozene (PCNB) (pentachloronitrobenzene)
Trade name: PCNB 75 WP and Terraclor 75 WP and Engage 75 W; PCNBIOG, Turfcide 10G and Engage 10G.
Manufactured by W. A. Cleary Chemical Corp., Uniroyal Chemical Co., Inc. and United Horticultural Supply. Product cleared for both greenhouse and outside use to control *Rhizoctonia* root rots as a protectant drench fungicide.
Legal usage: Broad legal use across flowering plants.
Comments: Active ingredient can damage some sensitive plants. If a second application is needed, use an alternative fungicide.

Thiophanate Methyl (4,4'-Phenylenebis[3-thioallophanate])
Trade names: Clearys 3336 (50%) WP, 3336-F (46.2%), Domain FL (46.2%), Fungo Flo (46.2%) and SysTec 1998 (46.2%).
Manufactured by W. A. Cleary Chemical Corp., (3336), Scotts-Sierra Crop Protection Co. (Domain and Fungo) and Regal Chemicals (SysTec). Products cleared for use in both greenhouse (except Fungo) and outdoors to control various foliar diseases caused by *Ascochyta, Botrytis, Cercospora, Phomopsis, Septoria,* etc. Also used as a drench for control of root/stem diseases incited by *Fusarium* and *Rhizoctonia* spp.
Legal usage: Broad legal use across flowers and ornamental plants.
Comments: Never spray or drench apply these products beyond two consecutive uses without alternating another product to minimize the risk of fungal tolerance development.

Vinclozolin (3-[3,5-dichlorophenyl]-5-vinyl-5-methyl-1,3-oxazolidine-2,4-dione)
Trade name: Ornalin FL (41.3%).
Manufactured by Scott-Sierra Crop Protection Co. Products cleared for use in both greenhouse and outside to control *Botrytis* flower blight and other foliar fungal diseases as a protectant spray.
Legal usage: For use on *Dendrobium* spp. only.
Comments: Do not spray on plants with less than three (3) leaves.

KEY: **F** = flowable; **gal(s).** = gallon(s); **lb(s).** = pound(s); **oz.** = ounce; **pt(s).** = part(s); **sq. ft.** = square foot; **Tbl.** = tablespoon; **tsp.** = teaspoon; **WDG** = water dispersible granules; **WP** = wettable powder.

Viruses and Their Control
By Roger H. Lawson, PhD

ORCHID ENTHUSIASTS BEGAN developing strategies to fight orchid viruses from the moment the first orchid virus disease was described in 1943. The last 59 years have seen the evolution of increasingly sophisticated, integrated programs to keep these tiny pathogens at bay. That evolution can be followed through editions of the American Orchid Society's *Handbook on Orchid Pests and Diseases*, first published in 1967.

In the first handbook, six virus diseases were described, but by 1975, when a revised edition came out, it was clear that only two viruses — cymbidium mosaic virus and tobacco mosaic virus — were responsible for all six diseases. Although these two viruses are still of primary importance, more than 20 additional viruses have been recognized in orchids in the ensuing years.

During that time, the best, and often only, defense against orchid viruses has been a strong offense. Chemical controls such as those used in bacterial and fungal diseases are ineffective because chemicals that inhibit viruses usually damage or kill the plant. Instead, maintaining good sanitation, buying clean stock, testing plants and destroying infected hosts have always been stressed as the keystones for successful control.

Several techniques exist to determine if a plant is infected. There are diagnostic

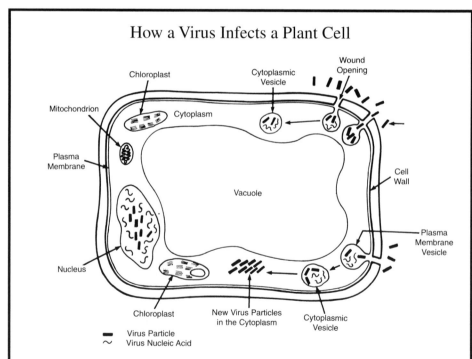

How a Virus Infects a Plant Cell

Chloroplast

Cytoplasmic Vesicle

Wound Opening

Mitochondrion

Cytoplasm

Plasma Membrane

Cell Wall

Vacuole

Plasma Membrane Vesicle

Nucleus

Chloroplast

New Virus Particles in the Cytoplasm

Cytoplasmic Vesicle

▬ Virus Particle
~ Virus Nucleic Acid

Virus particles enter the cell through wounds created by mild abrasion of the leaf surface. After entering the cell, the virus attaches to the plasma membrane and the protein coat is removed, releasing the virus nucleic acid. Vesicles containing virus particles separate from the plasma membrane and move into the cytoplasm. Newly formed virus particles are then released into the cytoplasm. Some viruses also multiply in the cell nucleus.

tests available, usually involving bioassays, serology or electron microscopy. Although bioassays and electron microscopy have remained largely unchanged since 1975, the use of new serological techniques such as the enzyme-linked immunosorbant assay (ELISA) increased the reliability and sensitivity of serological testing in the 1980s. During the 1980s, a new diagnostic procedure was also developed. This procedure, nucleic acid hybridization, resulted from recombinant DNA technology and offers the promise of significantly increased sensitivity.

Now, as we progress, prevention is still the best way to control orchid viruses, but new genetic engineering technology may soon revolutionize approaches to virus control. The best way to avoid a viral infection is to grow plants that are immune or resistant to the virus, something that previously has not been practical in orchid genera. Genetic transformation offers novel ways to develop virus-resistant orchids and the first research is already underway. Clean stock and sanitation will always be important, but plants may soon be defended against some orchid viruses by procedures that give permanent protection. See chart on pages 98 to 102.

What is a Virus?

Viruses have often been defined more for what they do than for what they are. Are viruses living or dead? If a biological life form is defined as one capable of reproduction, a virus fits the definition. If a living organism is defined as one capable of independent replication or reproduction, viruses are dead. Viruses can multiply only in the cells they infect.

Viruses are among the smallest disease agents so far described. Seen only with the aid of an electron microscope when magnified many thousands of times,

viruses remain some of the most important and destructive types of plant pathogens. More than 25 viruses have been reported infecting orchids. Most of these viruses are apparently separate and distinct disease agents.

Viruses are composed of nucleic acid and protein. The nucleic acid is the infectious portion of the virus particle while the protein provides a protective coat. Protection is necessary because the uncoated nucleic acid of the virus would be rapidly inactivated outside of the host cell.

Modern virology is a fascinating trail of scientific discovery beginning with the purification of tobacco mosaic virus (TMV) in the Nobel Prize-winning work of Dr. Wendell Stanley in 1935. TMV was the first virus shown to contain ribonucleic acid (RNA) as the genetic material responsible for infectivity. It was also the first virus to be reassembled in the test tube from its protein and RNA components.

TMV is one of the most studied viruses because it can be purified in such large quantities. It is estimated that 2.2 pounds (1 kg) of infected tobacco leaves can yield several grams of purified virus. TMV is also extremely stable in purified form or in infected tissue, even when dried. Infectious virus has been recovered from infected leaves dried for more than 30 years. A strain of TMV infecting orchids was recognized many years ago. This virus remains one of the most important and widespread disease agents in orchids worldwide.

The natural history of TMV includes extensive studies to establish the link between the virus' structure at the molecular level and its ability to infect a plant.

The Structure of Viruses

Viruses are composed of a regular structure that varies from a rod shape to a spherical form of particle. The principal virus particles in orchids have a regular size that varies from 300 nanometers (nm) long and 18 nm wide for orchid TMV (TMV-O) to the longer, 450 nm long and 13 nm wide particles of cymbidium mosaic virus (CyMV). (One nanometer is one millionth of a millimeter).

Much has been learned about the structure of viruses. The greatest number of plant viruses contain ribonucleic acid (RNA) as the agent of infection. All described orchid viruses are RNA viruses. Some viruses also contain deoxyribonucleic acid, but they mostly infect a narrow range of hosts. Particles of most plant viruses contain a linear piece of single-stranded RNA.

Most plant viruses contain only one type of particle while others include two or more particle types that contain different amounts of nucleic acid. Some of these different types of particles are not infectious on their own and require the other particles to reproduce. Symptoms of the disease may be influenced by the different types of particles and nucleic acids present in the infection.

Virus Replication

Viruses differ greatly from other cellular organisms in their method of replication. Bacteria, for example, reproduce by division. A single bacterium separates into two cells. During this process, both the old and new cells retain the appearance of the bacterial cell. In contrast, viruses multiply only in the living host cell. In the first step of this process, the virus particles are disassembled into their constituent parts. Many steps in the process of virus reproduction are poorly understood, but some information is available on how a virus interacts with the infected cell. After the virus enters the cell through a wound in a cell wall, or soon afterward, the RNA is released from the protein coat. A high concentration of

virus with many virus particles is required to establish infection. Inefficiency of the uncoating process may be why many particles are needed to produce an infection. It has been shown, for example, that much greater virus infectivity occurred when two to three percent of the protein was removed. It seems most likely that the virus particles attach to the plasma membrane in the plant cell where they enter the cytoplasm, or living-cell protoplast, by invagination of the membrane and formation of vesicles. Virus particles may also pass directly through the damaged membrane. It is known that intact virus particles of TMV can survive on the leaf surface and initiate infection over a much longer period than if isolated naked RNA alone is applied to the leaf.

Leaves infected with TMV RNA show a rapid virus synthesis. Infectious material, probably RNA, moves out of the epidermal cells into the underlying mesophyll. Infectious virus progeny can be detected at seven hours. After about 20 hours, most of the progeny RNA is coated with the viral protein. Each cell produces about one million to 11 million virus particles.

Effects of Viruses on Plants

Viruses cause a wide range of abnormalities that may change the form and appearance of the plant from the root tip to the shoot tip. Two of the most noticeable effects are yellowing (chlorosis) and death of the tissue (necrosis). These symptoms may occur separately or in combination.

Although viruses infect some species of plants only at the point of inoculation, where they invade cells near the wound site, most viruses systemically infect their hosts and cause much more damage. Viruses that systemically invade a host plant usually persist for the life of the plant. In vegetatively propagated plants, this persistence leads to widespread dissemination of cuttings or divisions that harbor the viruses.

Virus symptoms are variable and depend not only on the host species but on the strain of virus and environmental conditions such as light, temperature and nutrition. The time between infection and the appearance of symptoms also depends on the virus and environmental conditions.

Many viruses not only cause color changes in the host tissue, but they also restrict growth. Restricted growth often appears as stunting with reduced vigor.

Virus Symptoms in Orchids

Symptoms are highly variable among different orchid genera infected with the same virus. This variation may occur because of differences in plant response to infection or because of strain differences in the virus. Genetic factors are responsible for tolerance in some cultivars of a species and a high level of susceptibility in other cultivars. Because of this variation in symptom expression, it is often impossible to determine if a plant is virus-infected by the appearance of the foliage.

In spite of this variability in virus symptoms (due to genetic diversity within the orchid family), a grower should be aware of the types of symptoms most frequently associated with a particular virus in a particular genus.

Cymbidium Mosaic Virus

Cymbidium mosaic virus (CyMV) is the most widespread virus infecting a wide range of orchid genera. Foliar symptoms range from chlorotic streaks in many *Cymbidium* cultivars to black necrotic spots and necrotic line patterns with sunken patches in *Phalaenopsis* species. The necrotic spots and line patterns may appear dissimilar or the same on each side of the leaf. Necrotic symptoms may be produced in *Cattleya,* *Phalaenopsis, Dendrobium* and many other genera. Infected *Cattleya, Phalaenopsis* and *Dendrobium* species may, however, not show symptoms.

Virus-induced flower symptoms have been observed in CyMV-infected *Cattleya* species for many years. Flowers may show necrotic streaks within two to three days after the tight bud breaks open. More often, flower symptoms show after 10 to 12 days. For this reason, the disease is often unrecognized in recently opened

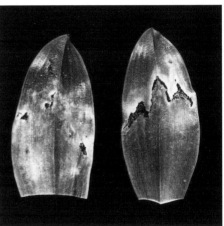

Phalaenopsis leaves infected with cymbidium mosaic virus showing necrotic spotting (left) and necrotic etching pattern on the upper surface.

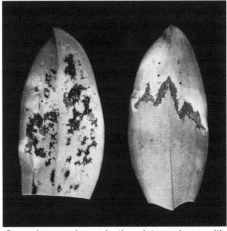

Same leaves shown in the picture above with extensive necrotic pitting (left) and the same necrotic line pattern (right) on the lower side of the leaf.

flowers at the time of harvest. CyMV-induced necrosis is usually most noticeable in white-flowered cattleyas (42). Similar symptoms develop in lavender-flowered cattleyas, but the brown necrotic reaction may be preceded by a sunken white cell necrosis appearing first along the midrib of the petal. Virus-induced flower symptoms are commonly observed on *Cattleya, Laelia, Dendrobium, Cymbidium, Phalaenopsis, Epidendrum* and *Vanda.*

Sunken necrotic spots on a leaf from a cattleya infected with cymbidium mosaic virus.

CyMV-infected orchids may not show foliage symptoms because of the virus strain, genetic tolerance of the specific host or because the environment is not conducive to symptom development. Orchids infected with CyMV may also not show symptoms if they are only recently infected. Although only a few controlled experiments have been reported, it seems clear that CyMV may not be detected until several weeks after infection. In one study, inoculation of pseudobulbs of cattleya seedlings with CyMV when the flower bud was first visible in the sheath resulted in necrosis in the flowers when the buds opened two to three weeks later. Rapid transport and multiplication of the virus was correlated with rapid growth and development of the flowering stem. Virus particles could not be detected in the inoculated leaves of the same plants until three months after inoculation.

Tobacco Mosaic Virus

The first strain of tobacco mosaic virus (TMV) isolated and identified from orchids was from *Odontoglossum grande.* The virus induced a ringspot symptom on the leaves and was named odontoglossum ringspot virus. Because this virus is a strain of TMV, it is referred to as an orchid strain or TMV-O. Although common, TMV has a wide host range and infects many different genera and species, TMV-O isolates infect only a few genera outside of the orchid family.

TMV-O induces a wide variety of symptoms in a range of orchid genera. Foliage symptoms include chlorotic and necrotic spots and streaks and rings. In lavender-flowered *Cattleya* cultivars, the foliage patterns are often associated with pronounced red or purple pigmentation. The leaf symptoms may appear as spots, chevron patterns or irregular line patterns of chlorotic or red-pigmented tissues. Leaves of *Oncidium* species may show a combination of sunken chlorotic and necrotic spots while *Epidendrum* shows only chlorotic spotting.

Flower breaking is consistently associated with TMV-O infection in lavender-flowered cattleyas. Streaks of dark pigmentation are often observed in lavender flowers in tight bud. The breaking symptom is apparent in the sepals and petals when the flowers open. Color-breaking patterns are often irregular in the same flower and differ among flowers in the same cluster. Some flowers in a cluster may show prominent color break while other flowers lack symptoms. The intensity and extent of virus-induced color breaking may also vary from year to year on the same plant.

Color breaking should not be confused with white streaks and patches that appear on the flowers of some lavender-flowered *Cattleya* hybrids. White-streak symptoms are caused by a genetic abnormality and have been identified in 25 to 30 percent of the crosses in seedling populations where one parent was a carrier of the white-streak genes. Infection by TMV-O in plants with white streaks in the flowers results in an increase in intensity of lavender pigment present at the margins of the white streaks. The presence of CyMV induces necrosis that appears as the flowers mature.

Tomato Spotted Wilt Virus

Tomato spotted wilt virus (TSWV) was first reported in 1992 from Hawaii (Hu et al., 1992). In California, impatiens necrotic spot virus (INSV) was reported in the same year (53). Although these viruses belong to the same group of Tospoviruses, they are not serologically related using conventional antiserum prepared in rabbits. This is important because in Hawaii only TSWV was identified and in California only INSV was reported.

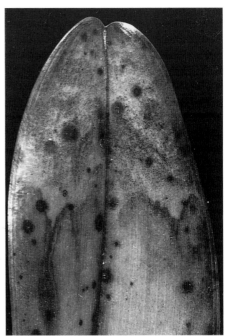

Red spots and line patterns on a leaf from a cattleya infected with orchid tobacco mosaic virus.

TSWV and INSV are of major economic importance. These viruses are known to infect more than 500 species of vegetable and ornamental plants. In addition to transmission by mechanical wounding in sap, these viruses are transmitted by thrips. *Frankliniella occidentalis* is a commonly occurring vector. TSWV was detected in *Oncidium* in Hawaii where *F. occidentalis* was also present. Because of the possible spread of the disease by the insect, care should be taken to control thrips and avoid growing virus-infected crops next to structures where orchids are grown.

The Need for Testing

Symptoms of virus infection may be confused with diseases caused by other types of pathogens or by physiological disorders. Water-mold fungi, such as *Pythium* and *Rhizoctonia*, cause rotting that often first occurs in the rhizome and spreads to the pseudobulb and the leaf.

79

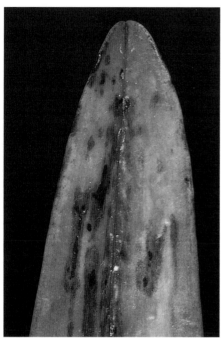

Spots and line patterns on a leaf from a cattleya infected with orchid tobacco mosaic virus.

Symptoms can include necrosis in the lower portion of the plant and stunting. In young plants, diseases caused by these fungi may result in rapid decline and plant death. Necrosis caused by virus diseases is usually not manifested as browning or discoloration in the roots and pseudobulbs. Virus symptoms, where they occur, are often most prominent on the leaves and/or flowers.

Many different leaf-spotting fungi infect orchids, and the lesions they produce may be confused with virus-induced symptoms. Although it is difficult to generalize, fungal-induced leafspots caused by fungi such as *Cercospora* species will produce fungal growth and spores on the discolored areas of the leaf they infect. Observation of a fungus in the discolored areas may be an indication of the presence of a fungal pathogen. This condition requires specific identification of the spores formed in the lesion since it is possible that nonpathogenic, saprophytic

fungi may grow and sporulate on tissue weakened by other causes, including physiological disorders.

Botrytis cinerea is a fungus that can cause serious petal blight of flowers. The disease is common in cool weather. Symptoms appear as discrete, small circular necrotic spots randomly spaced over the flower. In contrast, flower symptoms induced by CyMV appear first along the midrib, followed by the necrosis of the sunken spots developing farther from the vein.

Bacterial diseases can be serious. Diseases caused by bacteria, such as *Pseudomonas cattleyae* or *Erwinia carotovora*, can usually be distinguished from virus-induced diseases because they are frequently associated with water-soaking symptoms and rapid rotting of the crown and the affected leaves.

In addition to diseases caused by other kinds of pathogens, physiological and genetic disorders may cause chlorotic and necrotic spots in the leaves. Red leaf spots may be induced by high light intensity on healthy plants. The latter symptom is often observed on the leaves of lavender-flowered cattleyas.

Flower symptoms induced by air pollution may also be confused with virus-induced symptoms. The effects of ethylene on arresting development of flower buds and producing "dry sepal" injury are well known. Less well known, however, are the effects of other air pollutants that may be confused with virus symptoms. These pollution-induced symptoms may include white-cell necrosis or bleaching of the flower pigment. This appears as cleared spots on the sepals and petals and may appear similar to CyMV-induced symptoms on lavender cattleya flowers.

Insect feeding on foliage and flowers may produce sunken pinpoint spots where mechanical damage occurs. These spots may have associated areas of

Flower necrosis induced by cymbidium mosaic virus in a cattleya. Necrosis may appear as soon as four or five days after the tight bud breaks open but often appears 10 to 14 days after opening.

chlorotic or necrotic tissues in the leaves and altered pigmentation with increased intensity of color in the areas surrounding the insect feeding on the flowers. Thrips can cause symptoms resembling color break in vanda flowers.

Viruslike symptoms in orchid leaves, including chlorosis, spots, dots, tip and marginal burns, and scorching may have other causes. Nutritional and chemical imbalance, excessive salts in irrigation water, spider mites and scale insects, injuries due to insect feeding and pesticide spray damage may resemble or obscure virus-induced symptoms. Virus infection can only be established with certainty when the appropriate diagnostic test is applied.

Transmission of Orchid Viruses

Mechanical Transmission CyMV and TMV-O are efficiently transmitted in plant sap from infected to healthy plants when contaminated cutting tools are used to divide plants or harvest flowers. Bean yellow mosaic virus (BYMV), the small orchid rhabdoviruses, tomato ringspot, dendrobium mosaic, cymbidium ringspot, cucumber mosaic and tobacco rattle viruses can all be mechanically transmitted with differing efficiency. Although it is not known how efficiently these other viruses are mechanically transmitted from orchid to orchid, routine use of sterile cutting tools will greatly reduce the possibility of transmission.

Viruses may be transmitted from contaminated surfaces of pots and through water. Cattleya seedlings planted in sphagnum from pots previously containing CyMV and TMV-O-infected plants have become infected. Because virus particles and infectious virus have also been detected in water drained from pots containing infected cymbidiums and cattleyas (22), sanitation through proper sterilization of pots and tools is essential (see Control Through Sanitation).

CyMV and TMV-O are both spread through conventional vegetative propagation and tissue culture. Although virus-free cymbidiums have been produced in tissue culture from small shoot tips, virus-free cattleyas and many other orchid genera have not usually resulted. Recently, some success has been achieved in obtaining plants free of CyMV and TMV-O by treating small excised pieces of infected tissue with virus-specific antiserum at the time the tissue explant is removed and placed in tissue culture for future proliferation (29). This treatment may prove to be an important procedure for freeing orchids of CyMV and TMV-O.

Insect Transmission The green peach aphid (*Myzus persicae*) transmits some strains of BYMV, clover yellow vein, turnip mosaic, vanilla potyvirus, dendrobium mosaic and cucumber mosaic virus (63). Dendrobium vein necrosis is probably also aphid transmitted; however, CyMV and TMV-O (55), cymbidium ringspot virus (CyRSV) (18) and cymbidium mild mosaic virus (CyMMV) (5), are apparently not.

Aphid control is an important part of preventing the possible spread of several different viruses in orchids. Apply insecticide sprays as soon as the insects are evident. Separate affected plants to reduce the chance of aphids moving to other plants. Remember that CyMV and BYMV, both of which are aphid-transmitted, infect many crops other than orchids. Although the relationship between these strains and those infecting orchids is unknown, controlling aphids is always a good policy.

Control Through Sanitation

A strict sanitation program is necessary to prevent accidental transmission of viruses. This includes using clean tools. Heat treatment is the safest and most effective method of sterilizing tools. Reusable razor blades or knives can be heated in an oven at 300 F (149 C) for one hour. The most stable orchid virus, TMV-O, can be inactivated at temperatures of 205 and 212 F (96 and 100 C) after 10 minutes' treatment in orchid sap. It is important that the blade of the cutting tools reach the inactivating temperature within a few minutes after the treatment has begun. Propane torches may also be used to treat cutting tools. The tools are often dipped in alcohol before they are flamed. The cutting surface should be exposed to the flame for several seconds.

Liquid inactivating solutions can also be used to disinfect tools. Effectively using these disinfectants requires an understanding of their chemical reactions, however. For example, Clorox kills microorganisms and inactivates viruses because of its oxidizing power. A freshly prepared solution of two percent Clorox may completely inactivate CyMV but not TMV-O. A fresh 10 percent solution (10 parts of bleach added to 90 parts of water) will inactivate both viruses if tools are dipped for several seconds. The addition of plant sap to the Clorox solution

White cell necrosis induced by cymbidium mosaic virus in a lavender-flowered cattleya. The symptoms are not evident when the flowers open but appear one to two weeks later. In some cultivars the cells remain white and in others they become necrotic. This bleaching of the pigment may resemble air pollution damage.

decreases its effectiveness. If a large number of tools are dipped, the solution should be renewed frequently.

Rinse tools with running water at the end of each day. This will avoid buildup of plant sap on cutting surfaces and prevent formation of a protective layer that would prevent inactivation of the virus. Also, metal exposed to Clorox or other bleaches will corrode if the bleach is allowed to dry on the tool.

Clorox can also be used to soak pots. Before soaking in a 10 percent solution for 30 minutes to one hour, wash all soil and sap residue from the surface. After treatment, rinse the pots with running water.

A mixture of two percent sodium hydroxide and two percent formaldehyde has been recommended for treating cutting tools. The solution depends on alkaline degradation at high pH. A two percent solution of sodium hydroxide can reduce TMV-O infectivity by 86 to 96 percent. The value of adding formaldehyde seems doubtful because it breaks down to form formic acid and methyl alcohol with a resulting reduction in pH.

Trisodium phosphate is another good

Symptoms of severe color break in a cattleya flower induced by orchid tobacco mosaic virus. Note the increased pigment intensity commonly observed in lavender flowers.

virus inactivator because it produces a high pH in water solution. Be warned, however, that it is corrosive to metal tools and to exposed skin. A saturated solution of the chemical in water can be used as a dip for tools or as a soak for pots. Use the same time exposure as recommended for Clorox. Always wear protective gloves when using chemical disinfectants.

Disinfect benches previously containing diseased plants before reuse. Spray a solution of 10 percent Clorox or trisodium phosphate on the bench surface. TMV-O is stable and persists in plant debris for years. It is important to remove all debris and roots from the bench surface prior to chemical treatment.

Infectious strains of TMV are easily isolated from smoking tobacco, even though tobacco is flue-cured at elevated temperatures. In one study, cattleya seedlings inoculated with these tobacco isolates were not infected systemically with the virus. Nevertheless, avoid smoking tobacco and handling tobacco products when working with orchids. TMV readily mutates or changes to produce new strains. This could result in development of a new strain infecting orchids. Until more is known about the potential mutations in common strains of TMV that may become pathogenic to orchids, smokers should wash hands before dividing or handling plants.

Detection Methods

Three methods are useful in detecting and diagnosing orchid viruses: a plant test (bioassay), serological tests and electron microscopy. In this chapter, a detailed description of the bioassay procedure is presented. Results of serological tests for detection of CyMV and TMV-O from two commercial sources are compared. Detailed information on methods of serological testing and electron microscopy in orchid-virus detection are presented in this chapter of the AOS's *Orchid Pests and Diseases* (page 91).

Selecting a Test Sample The most important first step in detection is sample selection. Reliability of the test results depends on selection of tissue that is most likely to contain the highest concentration of virus. Usually, a small tissue piece is removed from a notch cut from the base of the leaf. Samples should be removed from two or three leads of different ages, including current season's growth, as well as two- to four-year-old growth. Leaf tips also can be used, but in plants recently infected, CyMV and TMV-O may be detected at the leaf base before they can be recovered from the tip. In specimens infected for a long time, the virus may be distributed more uniformly throughout the plant and the sample location may not be as important. Because recently infected plants may be only partially invaded, composite sampling from several sites on leaves of different ages is necessary.

Bioassay In a positive bioassay test, virus is transferred from the orchid being tested to another species that shows diagnostic symptoms. Specific symptoms on the leaves are characteristic of the virus tested. Extracts for inoculation of test plants are commonly made from leaves but may also be prepared from roots or flowers. Reactions indicating the presence of virus may appear as a yellow or brown necrotic spot on the leaves of a susceptible plant several days after the test extract is applied.

Although CyMV and TMV-O are the two viruses most frequently detected in this kind of test, bioassays are also widely used in certification programs for diagnosis of the short orchid rhabdovirus reported from Germany (47) and the orchid fleck virus in Japan (4). In addition, tomato ringspot, cymbidium ringspot, cucumber mosaic, bean yellow mosaic, dendrobium mosaic, tomato spotted wilt and impatiens necrotic spot viruses are detected in bioassay. A principal advantage of the test is its low cost. Seeds of test plants are easily propagated, and no special skill is required to perform the test — only a little practice.

Preparation of the Tissue Extract (Inoculum) The materials and equipment used to perform a bioassay are simple and inexpensive. They include 0.5 percent K_2HPO_4 (potassium phosphate), Carborundum, a mortar and pestle, and cotton swabs.

Remove a leaf, or portion of a leaf, with a razor blade. Cut each orchid with a fresh or sterile razor blade. The size of the tissue piece may vary, depending on the size of the plant and the lead to be tested. A notch can be cut about one-third the total width of the leaf and about $1/2$ to $3/4$ inch (12 to 19 mm) long on leaves of mature plants. Smaller leaf pieces should be removed from small plants.

Place tissue in a mortar and add a few drops of 0.5 percent K_2HPO_4 to the tissue pieces. Grind the tissue with a pestle to release the plant sap. This breaks open the cells and removes their contents. Although K_2HPO_4 does increase the infectivity of some viruses, it is not

Genetic white streaking in cattleya flowers caused by a genetic abnormality that is not associated with virus infection. This condition is inherited and may appear in crosses where one of the parents carries the white streak gene.

essential for infectivity, and tap water may be substituted if the phosphate is not available.

Method of Inoculation First, dust leaves of the bioassay test plant with an abrasive compound, such as Carborundum powder (silicon carbide crystals). The Carborundum forms small wounds in the leaf when the leaf is rubbed. The rubbing action carries the virus into the small wounds. Only a light dusting barely visible on the leaf surface is required. Too much Carborundum may damage the leaf surface if the leaf is rubbed vigorously.

Next, gently rub the orchid-juice extract over the leaf surface with a cotton swab. Remember to rub leaves dusted with Carborundum gently to avoid mechanical damage. If severe mechanical damage occurs, it will kill leaf cells, and nonspecific spots may appear on the leaves that are not due to a virus reaction.

One to two minutes after inoculation, wash the leaf with water to remove the excess inoculum. Positive tests will develop after a few days or up to three weeks, depending on the particular virus, the condition of the test plant and the environment in which the test plant is grown.

A plant test (bioassay) is one method for detecting and diagnosing orchid viruses. Once the tissue extract is prepared, dust the leaves of the test plant with Carborundum before inoculation. Carborundum is shaken onto the leaves from a bottle covered with two layers of cheesecloth. Only a small amount of Carborundum is applied to the leaf surface so that it is barely visible. An excessive amount will cause nonspecific mechanical damage and may obscure the virus symptom.

The Carborundum forms small wounds in the leaf when the surface is rubbed. Sap extract from an orchid leaf is rubbed on the Carborundum-dusted leaves of the indicator *Chenopodium amaranticolor*. The rubbing action carries the virus into the small wounds.

Indicator Plants for CyMV

Cassia occidentalis, Datura stramonium, Chenopodium amaranticolor, Chenopodium quinoa and *Tetragonia expansa* all show symptoms on the inoculated cotyledons or true leaves when rubbed with extracts containing CyMV. *Cassia occidentalis* is the most widely used test plant because uniform symptoms of virus infection are rapidly produced, regardless of differences in virus strain or environmental conditions.

Cassia occidentalis *Cassia occidentalis* is easy to grow. Plant six to eight seeds in a 4-inch (10 cm) pot filled with a light, composted soil. The seeds germinate after five to six days, and the cotyledons can be inoculated after nine to 12 days, before they are fully expanded. Round, rust-colored lesions are formed three to four days after inoculation on plants growing in a wide range of temperatures. Identical symptoms are produced by all CyMV strains that have been compared. Although older leaves may also be inoculated, many of the lesions do not enlarge and remain as very small, brown pinpoint spots.

CyMV does not systemically infect *Cassia* and plants may be grown for many months in the greenhouse, inoculating newly developing leaflets as the new growth appears. This procedure is most satisfactory in a warm climate where *Cassia* grows rapidly. In climate areas where *Cassia* grows more slowly, cotyledon inoculation is recommended. Mildew may be a problem on *Cassia*, but fungicide sprays can be employed without inhibiting the virus reaction.

Where high levels of air pollution occur, there may be a problem of nonspecific, pinpoint necrotic spots on the uninoculated leaves of *Cassia*. These nonspecific lesions are similar to virus lesions when they first appear, but can usually be distinguished from CyMV-induced lesions because the pollution-induced lesions remain small and do not expand. Include control plants that are either uninoculated or rubbed only with 0.5 percent K_2HPO_4 or water in all inoculation tests to identify any nonspecific spotting. If spots appear on the inoculated leaves of control plants, repeat the test.

Datura stramonium Datura, or Jimson

Cotyledons of *Cassia occidentalis* showing necrotic spots six days after inoculation. The lesions first appeared as small brown spots three days after inoculation.

weed, should be used as an indicator plant for CyMV with some caution because symptom expression may vary with different isolates of the virus and with environmental conditions. Also, *Datura* requires a relatively long growing period for the leaves to reach a length of 3 to 4 inches (7.5 to 10 cm) suitable for inoculation.

Datura may show three types of strain-related responses on green, nonsenescing leaves. The most common reaction is the formation of large, expanding necrotic lesions. The lesions usually appear after 15 to 23 days, depending on the age, leaf position on the plant and environmental conditions. Lesions on fully expanded leaves appear first as necrotic pinpoint spots and may expand up to $^3/_8$ inch (5 mm) in diameter. Some strains of CyMV form small, nonexpanding, necrotic lesions about $^1/_{16}$ inch (1 mm) in diameter or, in some instances, no symptoms at all on green leaves. All strains of the virus do produce lesions on leaves as the leaves senesce, as early as six to 10 days following inoculation. Necrotic lesions present on the green leaf may be surrounded by green halos and line patterns on the yellowing leaf. As symptomless, infected green leaves senesce, green rings and line patterns appear without associated necrosis.

Nonspecific pinpoint necrotic spots on the uninoculated leaves of *Cassia occidentalis*. The spots are caused by air pollution. They remain small and can usually be distinguished from lesions produced by cymbidium mosaic virus.

Temperature may also influence symptom development. In one study, *Datura* grown at a day temperature of 90 F (32 C) and a night temperature of 85 F (29.5 C) failed to show symptoms following inoculation with some CyMV isolates. Plants grown at a day temperature of 70 F (21 C) and 65 F (18.25 C) at night showed necrotic pinpoint lesions in 21 days.

Chenopodium amaranticolor and ***Chenopodium quinoa*** Both of these chenopodiums are susceptible to CyMV. Plants large enough to inoculate can be grown from seed in 30 to 40 days. They are inoculated when there are two to four leaves measuring about four centimeters at the base of the leaf blade.

Inoculated *C. amaranticolor* shows red or chlorotic rings and spots, sometimes with necrotic centers on green leaves. Because some strains of the virus form no

Leaf of *Datura stramonium* showing irregular-shaped necrotic spots 45 days after inoculation with a virus in a bioassay.

Chenopodium amaranticolor leaf showing symptoms of cymbidium mosaic virus. The lesions appear as green rings on a yellow background as the leaf senesces, 20 days after inoculation.

symptoms on green leaves, infection may be more reliably detected by observing the formation of green rings on the yellow background of senescing leaves. The rings appear six to 19 days after inoculation. High temperatures of 90 F (32 C) may suppress symptom development and reduce infectivity of some isolates of the virus.

Chenopodium quinoa is a more useful indicator plant than *C. amaranticolor* for CyMV detection. Symptoms are produced more uniformly, and it reacts with a wider range of CyMV strains. Small yellow lesions with red or tan necrotic centers develop 10 to 22 days after inoculation.

Indicator Plants for TMV-O

Cassia occidentalis, Gomphrena glo-bosa, Chenopodium amaranticolor, Nicotiana species, *Tetragonia expansa* and *Beta vulgaris* are all hosts of TMV-O. *Gomphrena globosa* and *C. amaranticolor* are the two species most commonly used to detect this virus.

Cassia occidentalis Local lesions in response to TMV-O infection are small and barely visible. They appear three to five days after inoculation as pinpoint necrotic spots that fail to expand on the inoculated cotyledons.

Gomphrena globosa Globe amaranth is a common ornamental grown in many gardens. The plant is easily propagated from seed. About 30 to 50 days are required to grow a seedling suitable for inoculation. Inoculate the plants in the four- to six-leaf stage when two sets of leaves are nearly fully expanded. In the greenhouse, with temperatures fluctuating from 65 to 75 F (18.25 to 24 C), TMV-O lesions first appear as pinpoint necrotic spots with surrounding inconspicuous chlorotic halos about four to five days

Cotyledons of *Cassia occidentalis* showing pinpoint necrotic spots induced by orchid tobacco mosaic virus. The lesions first appear after about three days and remain small and are often difficult to see.

after inoculation. Lesion development may be influenced by temperature. Large lesions appear about two weeks after inoculation on leaves of plants grown at 70/65 F (21/18.25 C) (day/night temperature), but only small lesions are produced at 90/85 F (32/29.5 C). The virus reportedly produces only local lesions on this host, but we have found that the new growth of plants subjected to 90 F (32 C) during the light period and 85 F (29.5 C) during the dark period is infected systemically after about two to three months. This host distinguishes between TMV-O and CyMV.

Uninoculated plants should always be maintained along with inoculated plants in each test. *Gomphrena* grown in high-light conditions may show red spotting that can be confused with virus-induced lesions. Therefore, grow *Gomphrena* test plants at 70 to 75 F (21 to 24 C) and at light levels of 1,500 foot-candles or less, so that conditions are optimal for virus-lesion development and minimal for non-specific spotting induced by the growing environment.

Chenopodium amaranticolor This plant is much more useful as a local-lesion host for TMV-O than as a local-lesion host for CyMV. Grow plants from seed as described under the section on CyMV bioassay procedures. TMV-O local lesion expression is also influenced by temperature on *C. amaranticolor.*

(Above left) *Gomphrena globosa* leaf infected with orchid tobacco mosaic virus showing large red spots with necrotic centers two to three weeks after inoculation on plants grown at 70/65 F (day/night temperatures), with 1,500 foot-candles fluorescent illumination. Large lesions are formed on leaves incubated at moderate temperatures.

(Above right) *Gomphrena globosa* leaf infected with orchid tobacco mosaic virus showing small necrotic lesions two to three weeks after inoculation on plants grown at 90/85 F (32/29.5 C) (day/night temperatures), with 1,500 foot-candles fluorescent illumination and supplemental incandescent illumination. Note suppression of lesion development at high temperatures.

Plants grown at 80 F (26.5 C) in a 16-hour light period with 1,400 foot-candles illumination and a 75 F (24 C) dark period showed faint yellow-spot lesions on the leaves six days after inoculation. Seven days after inoculation, plants grown during the 90 F (32 C) light period showed faint yellow-spot lesions, and those grown at 70 F (21 C) during the light period showed pinpoint necrotic spots. The centers of the yellow lesions on plants grown at 80 F (26.5 C) became

Leaf of *Chenopodium amaranticolor* (left) showing pinpoint chlorotic spots six days after inoculation with orchid tobacco mosaic virus. An uninoculated leaf is on the right.

Nicotiana glutinosa leaf showing necrotic spots six days after inoculation with orchid tobacco mosaic virus. The lesions remain small on this species but increase in size on *Nicotiana tabacum* Xanthi NN and *Nicotiana tabacum* Samsun NN Holmes.

necrotic pinpoints on the seventh day. In the greenhouse, with temperatures fluctuating from 60 to 80 F (15.5 to 26.5 C), the lesions were similar to those on plants grown in a 70 F (21 C) environment. Although TMV-O lesion development on *C. amaranticolor* depends on temperature, this host is a useful indicator for routine detection of the virus.

Nicotiana species, Tetragonia expansa and Beta vulgaris TMV-O induces brown necrotic lesions $\frac{1}{16}$ inch (1 to 2 mm) in diameter on the inoculated leaves of *Nicotiana glutinosa* about 10 days after inoculation. *Tetragonia expansa* shows chlorotic spots with necrotic rings on inoculated leaves five days after inoculation. *Beta vulgaris* 'Cicla' produces chlorotic local lesions in response to TMV-O infection.

Indicator Plants for
Short Orchid Rhabdoviruses

The short orchid rhabdoviruses can be detected by sap inoculation to *Chenopodium amaranticolor, C. quinoa, Petunia hybrida* and several species of *Nicotiana*, including *N. glutinosa, N. clevelandii* and *N. tabacum* var. Bright Yellow, White Burley, Xanthi nc and KY-57. For best results, perform inoculations in the summer when greenhouse temperatures are

86 F (30 C) or higher. Chlorotic spots develop on inoculated leaves of these host plants after two to four weeks.

Indicator Plants for
Other Orchid Viruses

The orchid isolate of BYMV from *Masdevallia* species is reported to infect *Chenopodium quinoa* and *Vicia faba* (broadbean). Tomato ringspot virus in *Cymbidium* species produces local lesions on the inoculated leaves of *Nicotiana tabacum* cv. Kentucky 35 and *Vigna unguiculata*. Cymbidium ringspot virus can be detected on *Emilia sagittata, N. clevelandii* and *C. amaranticolor*. CMV strains infecting *Dendrobium* may be transmitted to *Citrullus vulgaris* (watermelon), *Pisum sativum* (pea) and

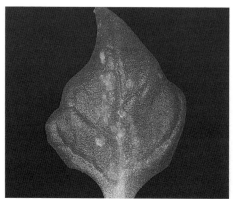

Upper leaf from *Tetragonia expansa* inoculated with orchid tobacco mosaic virus. Note the chlorotic spots and rings. Photo taken 35 days after inoculation.

Sesamum indicum (sesame). TomRSV in *Cymbidium* produces local lesions on the inoculated leaves of *Nicotiana tabacum* var. Kentucky 35 and *V. unguiculata.*

Producing a Virus-free Collection

A virus-free collection can be achieved. By virus-free is meant tested for all of the known agents of virus disease.

It is relatively easy to establish a virus-free collection when beginning a collection. Purchase plants only from growers who test their plants for viruses. As a prospective buyer, determine how the plants to be purchased were tested and how recently. Find out from the grower if the plants have been tested for CyMV and TMV-O and whether or not an evaluation has been made for any of the other orchid viruses. This is particularly important if one is purchasing an orchid from abroad where one of the other viruses listed in the chart of viruses is known to occur. As a matter of practice, it is a good idea to place all newly acquired orchids apart from the rest of a collection until the plant has been evaluated. If there is any indication of virus symptoms, test the plant or have it tested by one of the companies that offer this service.

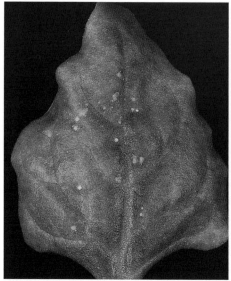

The older, expanded *Tetragonia* leaf shows necrotic spots that develop from chlorotic spots and rings as the leaf ages and yellows.

For an orchid hobbyist with an established collection, systematic testing should be the first priority in establishing a virus-free collection. First, test the oldest plants in the collection that have been previously divided. Old hybrids that have been in culture for many years are more likely to be infected with CyMV and TMV-O, the most common viruses.

At one time, many orchid growers thought that tissue-culture propagation was a method to produce virus-free plants as well as to propagate orchids vegetatively. Unfortunately, this is not generally true. Many different orchid genera remain virus-infected through the tissue-culture process. Before buying tissue-cultured plants, ask the propagator if the original orchid used for meristem culture was tested. When plants purchased from tissue culture are known to not have been tested, be sure to check them out.

Seedlings derived from green-pod culture may also be virused. In green-pod culture, tissue from the female parent is transferred to a culture medium where the seedlings develop. If the female is virus-infected, tissue that contains the virus is also transferred to the culture medium. In one report, one out of 123 dendrobium seedlings from green-pod culture was infected with CyMV when the female parent was infected (62). This report has not been confirmed, however.

Seedlings purchased for a collection probably have the greatest chance of being virus-free if they have not been divided or contaminated with cutting tools. Although both CyMV and TMV-O may be present in pollen, there is no evidence they are seed-transmitted in dry-pod culture. Young seedlings should be virus-free. Consider testing only if the plants show unusual symptoms.

Serology

Serological tests were first widely used in clinical diagnosis of many animal diseases. Serological diagnosis is now commonly used for detection of virus diseases of many vegetable and ornamental crops. Serological tests are specific, rapid and reliable.

Survival of an animal depends on an immune response that is an essential part of an organism's response to infection. The so-called immune response involves the interaction between an antigen, such as a virus or other microorganism, and a specific antibody that chemically reacts with the antigen. This chemical union is the basis for neutralization and elimination of the invading microorganism.

Many plant viruses have been shown to produce antibodies in experimental animals. Plant viruses induce the same type of immune response as animal pathogens. A plant virus injected into a test animal, such as a rabbit, produces specific antibodies that can be used to diagnose some important orchid-virus diseases.

Several types of serological tests have been used in the detection of orchid viruses. The chloroplast agglutination test is a simple procedure but no longer widely used because it is not as sensitive as new methods (41). A modification of this method using leaf discs in the agar wells has also been used (60). This method, known as the Ouchterlony agar double radial diffusion technique, is described as a grower-oriented technique.

The most widely used serological test method for detection of plant viruses is the enzyme-linked immunosorbent assay or ELISA. ELISA is a sensitive and specific procedure, detecting low concentrations of virus with minimum quantities of antiserum. Many samples can be processed at one time, and the procedure is suitable for large-scale testing. In the ELISA test, reagents are added in such a way that the enzyme-substrate reaction will occur only if the specific antibody-virus reaction occurs first. When the reaction is negative, the solution remains colorless. The ELISA method was described in the 1986 edition of this handbook.

ELISA Test Kits Serological test kits for detection of CyMV, TMV-O, tomato spotted wilt and impatiens necrotic spot virus are available commercially. Orchid growers interested in establishing a virus-free collection may either buy test kits or plants tested by a commercial company.

A comparison of these kits was made to see if they were sensitive and reliable enough for home testing. The names of the companies offering test kits were kept confidental. Here, only the types of tests and general conclusions are presented.

■ Test kits contained all of the necessary reagents in sufficient quantity to perform the number of tests designated by the manufacturer.

■ Instructions were complete, but for the uninitiated, the test may be difficult to perform unless the procedure has been observed step by step. One company included a videotape of the procedure. This type of teaching aid is useful.

■ Kits were significantly different in test sensitivity when they were compared using standard virus preparations. In one ELISA test, the color reaction for CyMV was only slightly above the background healthy control-leaf extract. The same virus preparation gave a strong positive reaction in the ELISA test kit supplied for CyMV detection by another manufacturer. Similarly, in a test for TMV-O, the kit from one source failed to show a positive reaction while the TMV-O preparation used in the test gave a strong positive reaction with a competitor's TMV-O test kit.

In conclusion, serological testing can be an excellent approach to virus diagnosis. A word of warning: Before spending time and money on a test kit, become familiar with the company offering the product. Established companies offer kits for detection of a wide range of different viruses. These companies have staff that can be consulted when problems arise. Or, as an alternative, serological testing services are now available commercially with a rapid turn-around time.

Electron Microscopy The electron microscope is an instrument that allows direct observation of the submicroscopic world. Capable of magnifying an object many thousands of times, the electron microscope provides a valuable tool for detection of viruses. Both CyMV and TMV-O can often be reliably detected using the electron microscope because they occur in high concentration in their orchid hosts. In fact, both CyMV and TMV-O can be detected in dilutions of plant sap that fail to reveal either virus in bioassay or serological tests (41).

The leaf dip is the most common method used to prepare samples for electron microscopy. First, a drop of electron-dense stain, such as sodium phosphotungstate at pH 7.0, is placed on a small copper support grid that has been coated

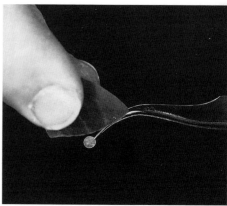

Preparation of a tissue sample for observation in the electron microscope using the dip method. The disc at the tip of the forceps is a 400-mesh copper grid covered with a Formvar film and a drop of two percent potassium phosphotungstate, pH 7.0. The exposed edge of the cut orchid leaf is dipped into the stain. Some of the virus particles remain on the grid surface when the preparation is dried down by removing the excess stain with filter paper.

with a plastic film. Samples are prepared by cutting the test leaf with a razor blade and placing the exposed cut surface on the drop of stain for one or two seconds. A fresh cut is made and the newly cut surface is placed on the drop of stain. The stain is then removed with filter paper until the grid is nearly dry. This wounding procedure will release virus from cells along the cut surface. The virus will float into the stain and many of the particles will remain on the grid surface when the drop is removed.

The sample is viewed in the electron microscope where rod-shaped virus particles will appear unstained with a darker background of stain surrounding the particles. Usually, only a few minutes of looking are required before virus particles are located.

In addition to CyMV and TMV-O, this technique can be used to detect other rod-shaped viruses, including bean yellow mosaic, dendrobium mosaic, dendrobium vein necrosis, cypripedium filamentous

Particles of cymbidium mosaic virus prepared by the dip method. Note the Flexuous structure of the particles. The particles are about 430 to 450 nm long. Magnification x53,000.

virus, turnip mosaic, tobacco rattle and vanilla mosaic viruses. Isometric viruses and bacilliform and bullet-shaped virus particles are much more difficult to detect. The particle shape of these viruses cannot always be easily distinguished from normal host plant contaminants.

Nucleic Acid Hybridization Complementary nucleic acids (cDNAs) to viral nucleic acids have been used to detect specific viruses and to differentiate between closely related viruses. cDNA is produced as a complementary copy of the viral RNA. The cDNA is then labeled with a radioactive probe (a chemical that detects the cDNA). When a viral RNA contacts its cDNA, the two molecules combine. The reaction is formed on a nitrocellulose membrane, and the membrane is exposed to film after extensive washing. A dark spot forms on the film where viral nucleic acid is present. The amount of radioactivity remaining on the membrane is related to the amount of viral nucleic acid bound to the membrane. Nonradioactive probes are now being developed for detection of the hybrid cDNA/viral RNA molecule.

Although this method is not in routine use for detection of orchid viruses, the procedure offers great promise. A practical method of detection would extract sap from an infected orchid plant and apply it to a nitrocellulose membrane. Labeled cDNA would next be applied. After washing the membrane, a reagent would be applied that gives a specific color reaction if the virus being tested is present.

Test Recommendations
All test methods described in this chapter may be successfully used to detect CyMV and TMV-O, although some are more useful than others. Because each procedure has certain inherent advantages and disadvantages, selection of a technique is based on individual circumstances and requirements.

Bioassay The bioassay method can be used by commercial growers and amateurs in their own greenhouses. No special skills or special equipment are required because test plants are easily grown and inoculation procedures are simple. The drawbacks: Symptom development on test plants may be influenced by environmental conditions and more than one species of test plant is required to detect more than one virus. Nevertheless, the bioassay is the least expensive test procedure and is recommended for general use, particularly in situations in which only a few plants are tested.

Serology Serological procedures are especially useful for large-scale testing because many samples can be tested at one time. The use of leaf discs and whole tissue pieces in agar gel double diffusion tests and ELISA represents a considerable saving in sample preparation time and labor. Reagents for these tests produced in kit form enable growers to test their own orchids and obtain results within 24 hours.

Serological procedures are specific, an advantage in some situations and a disadvantage in others. A negative result indicates only that the virus for the specific antiserum is not present. The presence of other unrelated viruses may be overlooked. If specific identification of a virus is required, antisera to more than one virus must be used.

Although serological testing is considered a laboratory test method, the ELISA procedure can be used successfully by both amateur and grower with some of the test kits currently marketed.

Electron Microscopy Many rod-shaped viruses can be detected with the electron microscope. The procedure itself is very rapid, taking only a few minutes per sample. Unlike serological techniques, however, only one sample at a time can be tested. Despite its many advantages, the electron microscope is an expensive instrument and availability of electron microscope testing services is limited. Electron microscope facilities may be available for testing on a fee basis at some universities.

Nucleic Acid Hybridization This procedure is being applied to detect several different viruses in nonornamental crops. It could be useful for detection of CyMV and TMV-O. Nonradioactive probes must first be developed, however, before the method can gain widespread use.

Genetically Engineered
Virus Resistance

Genetic resistance is the ultimate goal in protecting plants from virus diseases. Many vegetable crops and some ornamentals have been bred with resistance genes.

Virus-resistant plants are obtained by selecting and crossing appropriate parent plants and then selecting among the progeny for disease-resistant characteristics. Success depends on whether there is enough genetic variation in a crop to allow identification and incorporation of heritable resistance in new plant forms. In orchids, tolerance to cymbidium mosaic virus has been bred into *Dendrobium* hybrids (37). For most orchid genera, unfortunately, natural sources of virus resistance have not been identified.

Another form of resistance is induced resistance which is expressed only after it is activated by some external factor. These factors may include a previous virus infection, stress or aging. One form of induced resistance is the phenomenon of cross-protection. Cross-protection uses a mild virus isolate to protect plants against more destructive strain(s) of the same virus. As a natural control procedure, cross-protection has produced major improvements in the productivity of some crops. *Citrus tristeza* virus causes severe economic losses in many citrus-growing regions throughout the world. Several years ago the protective effect of naturally occurring mild strains against infection by more severe strains of citrus tristeza was discovered. Today, more than 30 million citrus trees are protected by pre-inoculation with these mild strains. Similarly, papaya trees have been successfully protected using mild strains of papaya ringspot virus. Although naturally occurring mild strains of papaya ringspot virus were not isolated from nature, chemically induced mild mutants of the virus were produced by exposing the virus to nitrous acid.

Cross-protection is associated with the virus's coat protein. The coat protein of the first viral strain suppresses additional infections when the same or related viruses are subsequently introduced into the plant.

Genetic Transformation

Recent advances in molecular biology and genetic engineering reveal that when noninfectious elements of viral genomes such as coat protein genes are introduced into the higher plant-cell nucleus, resistance to infection by the same or related viruses results.

Three potential problems in obtaining a transformed plant include:

■ The type of nucleic acid composing the virus.

■ The vehicle or vector for introducing

the foreign viral nucleic acid into the higher plant.

■ The expression of the viral nucleic acid introduced into the higher plant cell.

Type of Nucleic Acid Because genes in higher plant cells are composed of double-stranded DNA, the desired information from the viral gene must also be in this form. In the case of RNA viruses, this means that a DNA copy must first be made of the coat-protein gene. It is now possible to transcribe an RNA molecule into a complementary copy DNA (cDNA). The single-stranded cDNA molecule that is complementary to the viral RNA is then duplicated into a double-stranded molecule that is introduced into the vector molecule that can carry the viral gene into the plant cell.

Single-stranded DNA viruses are simply duplicated into a double-stranded DNA molecule that is transferred with an appropriate vector to the cell genome.

The Vehicle or Vector A major advance in genetic-engineering technology was made with the discovery that the bacterium *Agrobacterium tumefaciens* can transfer a defined piece of DNA (T-DNA) into the genome of a higher plant cell. This piece of DNA takes the form of a plasmid, a nonchromosomal DNA found in many bacteria. In nature, *A. tumefaciens* transfers a plasmid known as the tumor-inducing or Ti plasmid, into many dicotyledons to produce crown gall disease.

The strategy for development of Ti plasmid vectors depends on two properties of the DNA (T-DNA) that is transferred from *Agrobacterium* and stably inserted into the plant genes. First, the T-DNA is bounded by two directly repeating nucleotide sequences, called border sequences, that are essential for transfer to occur. Second, none of the genes located in the T-DNA between these border sequences is required for the transfer of this DNA. Thus, all of this DNA can be

deleted, and the coat-protein gene, along with a promoter for its expression and a kanamycin-resistance gene, can be added to the plasmid. The kanamycin gene serves as a marker for successful transformation. Only transformed cells will survive kanamycin treatment. Removal of the tumor-inducing capacity of the DNA permits normal development of the transformed cells after DNA transfer into the chromosome of the plant.

The traditional model for *Agrobacterium*-mediated transformation of dicotyledon plant tissues and subsequent regeneration of transgenic plants have been that of leaf-disc transformation of tobacco. This system permits efficient gene transfer along with selection and regeneration in a single process. Leaf discs or axenic explants are infected with the appropriate strain of *A. tumefaciens* carrying the vector of choice and cultured on a regeneration medium for two to three days. The virulent genes of the bacteria are induced during this time, and bacteria bind to the plant cells around the wounded edge of the plant tissue. Transformation occurs when the T-DNA is integrated into chromosomes of the plant nuclear genome. After transformation has occurred, the tissue explants are transferred to a regeneration/selection medium. The medium contains antibiotic to kill the bacteria and an appropriate antibiotic, usually kanamycin, to inhibit untransformed plant cells. This is shown in the accompanying illustration of the transformation procedure (see page 96). Transformed cells are allowed to grow into callus and differentiate into shoots. The small shoots that develop are removed then from the explant and rooted in another medium in preparation for transfer to a greenhouse. This transformation procedure has been used to transform more than a dozen genera from petunias to potatoes and even poplar.

Genetic Engineering a Virus-resistant Orchid

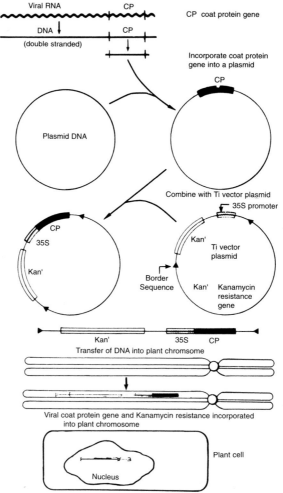

Virus-resistant plants are produced by incorporating the viral coat-protein gene into the chromosome of a plant. The process is initiated when the coat-protein gene is transferred into the DNA of a plasmid. The plasmid DNA is combined with the Ti vector plasmid from *Agrobacterium tumefaciens*. This plasmid contains a kanamycin-resistant gene and a promoter that are essential in the selection and transformation process. The Ti vector plasmid that now contains the coat-protein gene is transferred to the plant cell where it is incorporated into the plant chromosome and becomes part of the permanent genetic makeup of the plant.

Gene Expression in Transformed Plants

Expression of foreign genes in a plant that has been genetically engineered is essential if the newly transformed plant is to exhibit the characteristics of the original gene donor. Thus far, remarkable success has been achieved in the expression of the viral coat-protein gene of several different plant viruses. Reports on a variety of RNA viruses show that the presence of the genetically engineered viral-coat protein in the plant cells prevents or greatly slows infection. In tomato, for example, 10 to 15 percent of the plants expressing the coat protein of TMV did not show disease symptoms. This compared with 100 percent infection of controls. Similar results were reported with alfalfa mosaic virus. Plants expressing the alfalfa mosaic virus coat protein showed as little as 10 percent of the primary virus lesions found on nonexpressing plants.

The exact mechanism of protection using the virus coat-protein gene is unknown. It is known, however, that in the case of TMV, the invading intact virus is somehow prevented from removing its protein coat. Since the coat must be removed before the viral nucleic acid can replicate, blocking this essential step prevents infection.

Orchid Transformation

Success in transforming monocotyledonous plants using A. tumefaciens has been limited. Monocotyledons are normally not infected with this bacterium. Therefore, new procedures are being developed to transfer the DNA plasmid containing the coat protein gene into the nuclear genome of the orchid.

The first approach, which has been used to produce transgenic petunias, arabidopsis, rye and wheat, involves the direct injection of foreign DNA into actively growing meristems. The meristem is the shoot tip or root tip of a plant responsible for continuing growth and development. The second approach, which has been used to produce transgenic corn and rice, involves transforming seed. First, flowers are self-pollinated. When the pollen tubes contact the ovules in the ovaries, DNA containing the viral coat-protein gene is injected into the pollen tubes. Engineered cross-protection is a rapidly developing technology in the field of plant protection. It will be possible, in the near future, to develop virus resistance in many economically important plants, including orchids.

Although gene transfer in orchids has not been achieved, the coat protein chimeric gene of cymbidium mosic virus has been introduced into *Nicotiana benthamiana* through *Agrobacterium*-mediated transformation (6). These experiments were conducted to assess the possibility of using the virus coat protein gene to confer cross-protection. Results showed that over-expression of the CyMV coat protein could significantly reduce the virus titer in CyMV inoculated tobacco leaves. Since CyMV is not capable of infecting *N. benthamiana* systemically, it is not possible to determine whether the transgenic plants were tolerant to systemic infection by the virus.

Viruses Described in Orchids

Virus	Particle Morphology	Dimensions (nm)	Symptoms on Flowers	Means of Transmission	Local Lesion Hosts	Geographical Distribution	Place of 1st Record	Described by
Rod-shaped								
Cymbidium mosaic virus (CyMV)	Flexuous rods	415–475 × 13–18 (7, 12, 34, 40)	Necrosis of white colored cattleya flowers (39, 40, 41); color break in *Dendrobium superbum* (52); (syn. *anosmum*) white cell necrosis in lavender-flowered cattleyas (41)	Sap, nursery tools, pots and irrigation water (22)	*Cassia* species (7, 12, 30) *Chenopodium amaranticolor* (15) *C. quinoa Datura stramonium* (12) *Tetragonia expansa* (21, 23)	Worldwide (12, 33)	Australia 1943 (52)	Jensen (31)
Orchid tobacco mosaic virus strains including ORSV (TMV-O and ORSV)	Rigid rods	280–320 × 15–24 (8, 32, 38)	Dark color breaks (38)	Sap, nursery tools, pots irrigation water and plant debris (22)	*Chenopodium* species (34) *Gomphrena globosa Tetragonia expansa* (21) and some tobacco species (35, 59)	Worldwide (33)	United States 1951 (32)	Jensen and Gold (32)
Bean yellow mosaic virus (BYMV)	Flexuous rods	750 × 13 (26)	None reported	Sap and aphids	*C. quinoa* (3) *Vicia faba* (3)	Japan (25) United States (14) Germany (48, 50)	Japan, 1973 (26)	Inouye (26)
Dendrobium mosaic virus (DeMV)	Flexuous rods	750 × 13 (27	No symptoms	Sap and aphids	*C. quinoa* (27) *C. amaranticolor* (27)	Japan (25) United States (14)	Japan, 1971 (25)	Inouye (25)

Virus	Particle Morphology	Dimensions (nm)	Symptoms on Flowers	Means of Transmission	Local Lesion Hosts	Geographical Distribution	Place of 1st Record	Described by
Cucumber mosaic virus (CMV)	Isometric	30 (24)	Mild color break (24)	Sap and aphid	Chenopodium amaranticolor Citrullus vulgaris; D. stramonium and Sesamum (24)	Japan (24)	Japan, 1969 (24)	Inouye (24)
Cymbidium mild mosaic virus (CyMMV)	Isometric	28 (5)	None reported	Sap (5)	C. amaranticolor (5)	Korea (5)	Korea, 1978 (5)	Chang, Doi and Yora (5)
Trichopilia isometric virus (TI-virus unnamed)	Isometric	28	None reported	Not reported	Not reported	Germany	Germany, 1980	Lesemann (unpublished)
Masdevallia isometric virus (MI-virus unnamed)	Isometric	Not reported	Not reported	Mechanical transmission not successful (44)	Not reported	Colombia (44)	Colombia, 1981 (44)	Lesemann (44)
Tomato ringspot virus (TomRSV)	Isometric	30 (13)	Not reported	Sap (to indicator species but not back to orchid)	Nicotiana tabacum var. Kentucky 35, Vigna unguiculata (13)	United States (13)	United States, 1977 (13)	Goff and Corbett (13)

Bacilliform and Bullet-shaped Viruses
(Small Rhabdovirus-type Viruses)

Virus	Particle Morphology	Dimensions (nm)	Symptoms on Flowers	Means of Transmission	Local Lesion Hosts	Geographical Distribution	Place of 1st Record	Described by
Short orchid rhabdovirus (KORV)	Bullet-shaped bacilliform	47 × 105 (47)	None reported	Sap (47)	C. quinoa (47) C. amaranticolor N. clevelandii	Denmark (45) Germany (47)	Denmark, 1971 (45)	Lesemann and Doraiswamy (47), Lesemann and Begtrup (45)

Virus	Particle Morphology	Dimensions (nm)	Symptoms on Flowers	Means of Transmission	Local Lesion Hosts	Geographical Distribution	Place of 1st Record	Described by
Clover yellow vein virus (CYVV-C)	Flexuous rods	750 × 12 (28)	Necrosis	Sap and aphids	*Vicia faba, Pisum sativum* (28)	Japan (28)	Japan, 1988 (28)	Inouye (28)
Dendrobium vein necrosis virus (DVN)	Flexuous rods	1865 (43)	Veinal necrosis (43)	None reported	None reported	Germany (43) United States (63)	Germany, 1977 (43)	Lesemann (43)
Cypripedium filamentous virus (CF-virus unnamed)	Flexuous rods	772 (49)	None reported	Mechanical transmission unsuccessful (49)	None	Germany (49)	Germany, 1980 (49)	Lesemann and Koenig (49)
Turnip mosaic virus	Flexuous rods	745 (51)	None reported	Sap and aphids	*Nicotiana clevelandii* (51) *C. quinoa* (51)	Germany (51)	Germany, 1985 (51)	Lesemann and Vetten (51)
Tobacco rattle virus (TRV)	Rigid rods	65 and 193 (51)	Misshaped flowers	Sap	*Nicotiana tabacum* cv. Xanthi (51)	Germany (51)	Germany, 1985 (51)	Lesemann and Vetten (51)
Vanilla mosaic virus	Flexuous rods	767 (61)	None reported	Aphids	None reported	French Polynesia (61)	French Polynesia 1987 (61)	Wisler, Zettler and Mu (61)
Isometric								
Cymbidium ringspot virus (CyRSV)	Isometric	30 (17)	None reported	Sap, soilborne	*Chenopodium amaranticolor Emilia sagittata* (16 *Nicotiana clevelandii* (15), *Phaseolus vulgaris*	England (16, 18, 19)	England, 1963 (16)	Hollings and Stone (16, 17, 18)

Virus	Particle Morphology	Dimensions (nm)	Symptoms on Flowers	Means of Transmission	Local Lesion Hosts	Geographical Distribution	Place of 1st Record	Described by
Dendrobium virus (DV)	Bullet-shaped bacilliform	50 × 120 (2)	None reported	None reported	None reported	D. inoglossum from New Guinea (2), Germany (11, 60)	Germany, 1971 (60)	Petzold (60) Duvel and Peters (11)
Orchid fleck virus (OFV)	Bullet-shaped bacilliform	40 × 150 (4)	None reported	Sap. at temperatures 86 F (30 C) (4)	C. amaranticolor C. quinoa, N. tabacum, N. glutinosa (4, 10)	Japan (10)	Japan, (10)	Chang, Arai, Doi and Yora (4)
Unnamed rhabdovirus (RV-virus unnamed)	Rodlike	40 × 100–120 (36)	None reported	None reported	None reported	Brazil (36)	Brazil, 1974 (36)	Kitajima, Blumenschein and Costa (36)
Grammatophyllum bacilliform virus (GBV)	Bullet-shaped, bacilliform	40–42 wide particles with variable length (9)	None reported	None reported	None reported	Maryland (United States) (9)	Maryland, 1974	Corbett (9)

Large Rhabdovirus-type Viruses

Virus	Particle Morphology	Dimensions (nm)	Symptoms on Flowers	Means of Transmission	Local Lesion Hosts	Geographical Distribution	Place of 1st Record	Described by
Dendrobium rhabdovirus (DRV)	Bullet-shaped bacilliform	180, 320 × 85 (1)	White streak but CyMV also present and effect of bacilliform virus alone unknown (1)	None reported	None reported	Hawaii (United States) (1)	Hawaii, 1974 (1)	Ali, Lawson and Ishii (1)
Long orchid rhabdovirus (LORV)	Bullet-shaped bacilliform	176 × 83 (48)	None reported	None reported	None reported	Germany (48)	Germany, 1975 (48)	Lesemann and Doraiswamy (48)

Virus	Particle Morphology	Dimensions (nm)	Symptoms on Flowers	Means of Transmission	Local Lesion Hosts	Geographical Distribution	Place of 1st Record	Described by
Laelia red leafspot virus (LRLSV)	Bullet-shaped bacilliform	190–220 × 80 (57)	None reported	None reported	None reported	Germany (57)	Germany, 1977 (57)	Peters (57)
Tomato spotted wilt virus	Quasispherical	85	None reported	Sap and thrips	*Petunia hybrida* *N. benthamiana*	Hawaii (United States) (20)	Hawaii, 1992 (20)	Hu et al. (20)
Impatiens necrotic spot virus	Quasispherical	85	None reported	Sap and thrips	*Petunia hybrida* *N. benthamiana*	California (United States)	California, 1992 (53)	Mayhew, Cooke and Raabe (53)
Other								
Unnamed bacilliform virus from Phalaenopsis (PhBV-virus unnamed)	Bacilliform	119 × 29 (49)	None reported	None reported	None reported	Germany (49)	Germany, 1980 (49)	Lesemann and Koenig(49)

References

1. Ali, S., R. H. Lawson, and M. Ishii.1974. A bacilliform virus in white-streaked *Dendrobium phalaenopsis* flowers. *Amer. Orchid Soc. Bull.* 43:529-533.
2. Begtrup, J. 1972. Structure of a bacilliform virus in *Dendrobium* as revealed by negative staining. *Phytopathol. Z.* 75:268-273.
3. Bos, L. 1970. Bean yellow mosaic virus. CMI/AAB. *Description of Plant Viruses* No. 40.
4. Chang,M. U., K. Arai, Y. Doi, and K. Yora.1976. Morphology and intracellular appearance of orchid fleck virus. *Ann. Phytopathol. Soc. Japan* 42:156-157.
5. ___, Y. Doi, and K. Yora. 1978. Cymbidium mild mosaic virus, isolation of cymbidium mild mosaic virus. *Korean J. Plant Prot.* 17:131-138.
6. Chia, Tet-Fatt, Yang-Sun Chan, and Nam-Hai Chua. 1992. Characterization of cymbidium mosaic virus coat protein gene and its expression in transgenic tobaco plants. *Molecular Plant Biology* 18:1091-1099.
7. Corbett, M. K. 1960. Purification by density gradient centrifugation, electron microscopy, and properties of cymbidium mosaic virus. *Phytopathology* 50:346-351.
8. ___. 1967. Some distinguishing characteristics of the orchid strain of tobacco mosaic virus. *Phytopathology* 57:164-172.
9. ___. 1974. Intranuclear bacilliform virus-like particles in *Grammatophyllum scriptum*. *Phytopathology* (Abstr.). Potomac Div. Meeting of Amer. Phytopathol. Soc., March 28-29, 1974.
10. Doi,Y., M. U. Chang, and K. Yora. 1977. Orchid fleck virus. CMI/AAB. *Description of Plant Viruses* No. 183.
11. Duvel, D., and K. R. Peters. 1971. Virusahnliche partikel in *Dendrobium antennatum Ldl.* *Gartenwelt* 71:52-54.
12. Francki, R. I. B.1970. Cymbidium mosaic virus. CMI/AAB. *Description of Plant Viruses* No. 27.
13. Goff, L. M., and M. K. Corbett. 1977. Association of tomato ringspot virus with a chlorotic leaf *Phytopathology* 67:1096-1100.
14. Hammond, J., and R. H. Lawson. 1988. A strain of bean yellow mosaic virus is aphid-transmitted from orchid. *Acta Horticulturae* 234:365-370.
15. Hollings, M. 1966. Local lesion and other test plants for the identification and culture of viruses Pages 230-241 *in* A. B. R. Beemster and J. Dijkstra (eds.), *Viruses of Plants*, North Holland Publishing Co., Amsterdam.
16. ___, and O. M. Stone. 1963. Cymbidium ringspot (a previously undescribed virus). *Glasshouse Crops Res. Inst. Ann. Report,* page 89.
17. Hollings, M. 1972. Orchids — Cymbidium ringspot. *Glasshouse Crops Res. Inst. Ann. Report.*, page 104.
18. ___. 1977. Cymbidium ringspot virus. CMI/AAB. *Description of Plant Viruses* No. 178.
19. ___, O. M. Stone, and R. J. Barton. 1977. Pathology, soil transmission and characterization of cymbidium ringspot, a virus from cymbidium orchids and white clover (*Trifolium repens*). *Ann. Appl. Biol.* 85:233-248.
20. Hu, J. S., M. Wang, S. Ferreira, and D. Ogata. 1992. Tomato spotted wilt virus on *Oncidium* orchids in Hawaii. *Plant Disease* 76:426.
21. Inouye, N. 1965. Virus diseases of orchids. II. Symptoms and properties of viruses in *Cymbidium*. *Japan Orchid Soc. Bull.* 11:1-6.
22. ___. 1968a. Some experiments on the transmission of cymbidium mosaic virus and odontoglossum ringspot virus. *Nogaku Kenkyu* 52:89-97.
23. ___. 1968b. Virus diseases of *Cymbidium* and *Cattleya* caused by cymbidium mosaic virus. *Ber. Ohaara Inst. Landw. Biol. Okayama Univ.* 14:161-170.
24. ___. 1969. Cucumber mosaic virus isolated from *Dendrobium. Agric. Res. (Kurashiki)* 53:49-60.
25. ___. 1971. Virus diseases of orchids. V. Symptoms and properties of viruses in *Dendrobium*. *Japan Orchid Soc. Bull.* 17:3-7.
26. ___. 1973. A new virus isolated from *Dendrobium. Ann. Phytopathol. Soc. Japan* 39:367-368.
27. ___. 1976. *Dendrobium* mosaic virus. *Ber. Ohara Inst. Landw. Biol. Okayama Univ.* 16:165-174.
28. ___, T. Maeda, and K. Mitsuhata. 1988. A strain of clover yellow vein virus isolated from *Calanthe* sp. *Acta Horticulturae* 234:61-68.
29. ___. 1983. Effect of antiserum treatment on the production of virus-free *Cymbidium* by means of meristem culture. *Nogaku Kenkyu* 60:123-133.
30. Isadpanah, K. M., R. Thompson, and H. H. Thornberry. 1966. A simple method for detection of a flexous-rod virus associated with infectious *Cattleya blossom* necrosis. *Pl. Dis. Reporter* 50:779-781.
31. Jensen, D. D. 1951. Mosaic or black streak diseases of *Cymbidium* orchids. *Phytopathology* 41:401-414.
32. ___, and A. H. Gold. 1951. A virus ringspot of *Odontoglossum* orchid: Symptoms, transmission and electron microscopy. *Phytopathology* 41:648-653.
33. ___. 1970. Virus diseases of Orchids in the Netherlands. *Netherlands J. Pl. Pathol.* 76:135-139.
34. Kado, C. I., and D. D. Jensen. 1964. Cymbidium mosaic virus in *Phalaenopsis. Phytopathology* 54:974-977.
35. ___, M. H. V. van Regenmortel, and C. A. Knight. 1968. Studies on some strains of tobacco mosaic virus in orchids. 1. Biological, chemical, and serological studies. *Virology* 34:17-24.
36. Kitajima, E. W., A. Blumenschein, and A. S. Costa. 1974. Rodlike particles associated with ringspot symptoms in several orchids species in Brazil. *Phytopathol. Z.* 81:280-286.
37. Kobayashi, R. S., and H. Kamemoto. 1989.

Inheritance of floral necrosis in *Dendrobium* induced by cymbidium mosaic virus. *Hort. Sci.* 24:499-500.

38. Lawson, R. H. 1970. Virus-induced color breaking in *Cattleya* orchid flowers. *Amer. Orchid Soc. Bull.* 39:395-400.

39. ___. 1970. Flower necrosis in *Cattleya* orchids. *Amer. Orchid Soc. Bull.* 39:306-312.

40. ___. 1970. Etiology of flower necrosis in *Cattleya* orchids. *Phytopathology* 60:36-40.

41. ___, and M. Brannigan. 1986. Virus diseases of orchids. Pages 2-49 *in Handbook on Orchid Pests and Diseases* (revised edition). American Orchid Society, West Palm Beach, Florida.

42. ___, and S. S. Hearon. 1973. Symptomatology of *Cattleya* mericlones infected with cymbidium mosaic virus. *Amer. Orchid Soc. Bull.* 42:1071-1074.

43. Lesemann, D. E. 1977. Long, filamentous virus-like particles associated with vein necrosis of *Dendrobium phalaenopsis*. *Phytopathol. Z.* 89:330-339.

44. ___. D. E. 1981. Virus diseases in orchids: diagnosis, distribution, etiology, epidemiology. *Annual Rep. Biologische Bundesanstalt fur Land-und Forstwirtschaft in Berlin und Braunscheig*. No. 13:H58.

45. ___, and J. Begtrup. 1971. Elektronenmikroskopische nachweis eines bazilliformen virus in *Phalaenopsis*. *Phytopathol. Z.* 71: 257-269.

46. ___, and S. Doraiswamy. 1975. Bullet-shaped virus-like particles in chlorotic and necrotic leaf lesions of orchids. *Phytopathol. Z.* 83:27-39.

47. ___, and S. Doraiswamy. 1975. Nachweis und elektronmikroskopische charakterisierung von "langen," bullet-forminge viruspartikeln in kultivierten orchideen. *Phytopathol. Z.* 84:201-214.

48. ___, and R. Koenig. 1978. Virus diseases in orchids: diagnosis, distribution, etiology, epidemiology. *Annual Rep. Biologische Bundesanstalt fur Land-und Forstwirtschaft in Berlin und Braunschweig*. No. 24:H70.

49. ___. 1980. Virus diseases in orchids: diagnosis, distribution, etiology, epidemiology. *Annual Rep. Biologische Bundesanstalt fur Land-und Forstwirtschaft in Berlin und Braunschweig*. No. 14:H61.

50. ___. 1985. Identification of bean yellow mosaic virus in *Masdevallia*. *Acta Horticulturae*. 164:347-354.

51. ___, and H. J. Vetten. 1985. The occurrence of tobacco rattle and turnip mosaic viruses in *Orchis* sp., and of an unidentified potyvirus in *Cypripedium calceolus*. *Acta Horticulturae* 164:45-54.

52. Magee, C. J. 1943. Orchid mosaic. *Austral. Orchid Rev.* 8:51-52.

53. Mayhew, D.E., A.L. Cooke, and R.D. Raabe. 1992. Special report. A new virus is reported for *Phalaenopsis*. *Amer. Orchid Soc. Bull.* 61:574-577.

54. Murakishi, H. H. 1952. Transmission of a leaf mosaic associated with color break in the flowers of *Dendrobium superbum* Reichb. f. *Phytopathology* 42:339-340.

55. Namba, R., and M. Ishii. 1971. Failure of aphids to transmit the odontoglossum ringspot and cymbidium mosaic viruses to orchid plantlets derived from meristem cultures. *Phytopathology* 61:582-583.

56. Pearson, M. N., and J. S. Cole. 1986. The effects of cymbidium mosaic virus and odontoglossum ringspot virus on the growth of *Cymbidium* orchids. *J. Phytopathol.* 117:193-197.

57. Peters, K. R. 1977. Orchid viruses: a new rhabdovirus in *Laelia* red leafspots. *J. Ultrastruct. Res.* 58:166-171.

58. Petzold, H. 1971. Der elektronenmikroskopische nachweis eines bazilliformen virus an blattfleckenkranken dendrobien. *Phytopathol. Z.* 70:43-52.

59. Thompson, A. D., and B. A. Smirk. 1967. An unusual strain of tobacco mosaic virus from orchids. *New Zealand J. Bot.* 5:197-202.

60. Wisler, G. C. 1989. *How to Control Orchid Viruses: The Complete Guidebook*. Waupin House Publishers, Gainesville, Florida.

61. ___, G. C., F. W. Zettler, and L. Mu. 1987. Virus infections of Vanilla and other orchids in French Polynesia. *Pl. Disease* 71:1125-1129.

62. Yuen, C.K.K.H., H. Kamemoto, and M. Ishii. 1979. Transmission of cymbidium mosaic virus through seed propagation in *Dendrobium*. *Amer. Orchid Soc. Bull.* 48:1245-1247.

63. Zettler, F. W., G. C. Wisler, M. S. Elliott, and N. J. Ko. 1987. Some new, potentially significant viruses of orchids and their probable means of transmission. *Amer. Orchid Soc. Bull.* 56:1044-1051.

Glossary
By Gary W. Simone, PhD, Donald E. Short, PhD, and R.A. Dunn, PhD

Absorption The penetration of a chemical (pesticide) into a plant, pest species or through the skin.

Active Ingredient The biologically active and pure toxic component of a chemical formulation (pesticide).

Acute Exposure This is a one-time exposure to a pesticide resulting in injury or death that is directly attributable to the pesticide.

Adjuvant Any component of a pesticide formulation (e.g., stickers or emulsifiers) that modifies the activity of the pesticide in a positive sense.

Adsorption The binding of a chemical (pesticide) to the outside surface of small soil particles or organic matter.

Aerosol A pesticide formulation that suspends a liquid or solid chemical in a gas carrier.

Antibiotic A complex chemical produced by one microorganism that has been found to inhibit or kill another microorganism. An example of an antibiotic pesticide is Agrimycin 17 (streptomycin sulfate).

Antibody A protein that is produced by warm-blooded animals in response to injected antigen. The antibody-containing serum (antiserum) is separated from test-animal blood and used to diagnostically detect a specific antigen (plant virus).

Application Rate The amount of a pesticide to be applied per volume of diluent per unit area or per plant.

Attractant A substance used to attract destructive pests (animals, insects) that is usually mixed with a killing agent or trap.

Bactericide A pesticide that kills bacteria.

Bacterium A microscopic, one-celled organism that lacks a true nucleus and chloroplasts. Some may cause plant disease when they enter natural openings or wounds in plant tissue.

Basic Copper Sulfate This is a fungicide-grade of chemical that is distinct from blue-stone or blue vitriol in that its chemical formula is $CuSo_4.3H_2O$ and has a greater margin of plant safety.

Biological Control The control of pests by using predacious or parasitic organisms (insects, nematodes, bacteria, fungi, viruses).

Blight The rapid decline and death of plant parts. This term is often used with the name of a pathogen or the name of the host part affected (Botrytis blight, blossom blight).

Blister A symptom consisting of a localized bulge or bubblelike eruption from foliar plant tissue that typically has a concave lower leaf surface. This symptom is commonly caused by a group of fungal plant diseases (oak-leaf blister) but may also be induced by certain insects or pesticide phytotoxicity.

Broad-spectrum When applied to a pesticide, denotes a wide range of pest species controlled (e.g., metam sodium).

Broadcast Application The application of any pesticide in a uniform manner over an entire area, as contrasted to band application.

Burn A condition in which localized areas of foliar plant tissue become damaged, resulting in a reddish to dark brown discoloration followed by cell collapse.

Carcinogen A substance that will produce cancer in a test animal.

Carrier Some inert material (dust, clays, oils) mixed with a pesticide to improve the uniform dispersal of the pesticide.

Caution This term on a pesticide label means the pesticide in question is of low toxicity with an oral LD_{50} of greater than 500 mg/kg and a dermal LD_{50} of greater than 1000 mg/kg. Use protective clothing and breathing devices under conditions of prolonged use.

Chemical Compatibility When two or more chemicals can be mixed together without adverse effects, such as precipitation, loss of individual product activity or loss of plant safety.

Chemtrec This is a toll-free, long distance telephone service that provides 24-hour emergency pesticide assistance (800-424-9300) as regards pesticide transport, storage, spill cleanup, etc.

Chlorosis The yellowing or whitening of green plant parts as a result of chlorophyll break-down or production failure. This condition can be caused by microbe or pest attack (i.e., disease) or a number of abiotic factors such as soil pH, soil fertility or moisture.

Color Break A viral-disease symptom to describe the discoloration of flowers as evidenced by a change in intensity of color and/or pattern. Color break may also result from genetic mutation.

Compatibility In reference to pesticides, the mixture of two or more pesticides together without reducing their effectiveness against the pests or causing injury to the plants.

Crown Rot Disease type where the pathogen infects the host plant at the soil line, girdling and killing the plant.

Curl Disease symptom describing the distortion or puckering of a leaf due to uneven growth of the two sides.

Damping-off Seed decay in the soil or seedling death prior to or after emergence. Seedlings wilt, topple and die. Soilborne fungal pathogens are the typical cause.

Danger Signal word used with "POISON" and a skull and crossbones symbol used on pesticide labels to designate the highest toxicity class (1) for that particular product. These products are characterized by having an oral LD_{50} value of 0-50 mg/kg and a dermal LD_{50} =0-200 mg/kg.

Dieback The progressive death of shoot or branch tips. This symptom may be caused by a root or stem related disease, insect injury, nematode feeding and a number of abiotic factors such as winter injury or moisture stress.

Disease Any deviation from the normal growth, structure or quality of a plant that is a continuous condition that produces symptoms, thus affecting the economic quality or value of that plant. Diseases can be caused by a variety of pathogenic organisms as well as improper environmental conditions.

Disinfectant Any material, such as hot water or systemic pesticides, that will kill pathogens once they have infected a plant or plant parts.

Dry Flowable (DF) Dry-flowable formulations are sprayable, solid pesticide formulations that are improvements over wettable powder types by offering improved solubility and less dust hazard during mixing.

Ectoparasitic Referring to nematodes that spend all of their life cycle outside of the plant tissues on which they feed. All four juvenile stages and adults can move freely about the surface of the root and through soil to seek feeding sites. They often focus on root tips and other especially tender tissues.

ELISA (Enzyme-linked immunosorbent assay) A serological diagnostic technique wherein the antibody is linked with an enzyme that results in a color reaction in the presence of the correct antigen (virus, etc.).

Emulsifiable Concentrate (EC) A liquid pesticide formulation that is mixed with water to form an emulsion.

Emulsion A mixture of a pesticide (in liquid form) as small globules in water.

Endoparasitic Referring to nematodes that spend at least part of their life cycle entirely within the plant tissues on which they feed. *Migratory* endoparasites typically feed and live in relatively tender cortical tissues; all stages except the egg are mobile. *Sedentary* endoparasites generally have only one juvenile stage and adult males able to move; advanced juvenile stages and adult females are immobile, depending on a few specially modified plant cells to feed them throughout their existence.

Eradicant A control measure (pesticidal or physical) that kills the pathogen after its establishment in a host plant.

Exudate A plant product (often a liquid) that is released from inside the plant through diseased or injured plant areas. Exudates are often diagnostic for certain diseases like gummy stem blight of cucurbits.

Facultative Parasite An organism that has the ability to parasitize another living organism but normally survives independently of other life forms.

Flowable (F) This formulation of a pesticide is a finely ground wettable powder sold as a thick suspension in a liquid to facilitate mixing with water.

Fungicide A group of organisms that destroys or inhibits fungal pathogens that cause plant disease. Fungicides are most often used as protectants on plants but can be used as disinfectants and eradicants.

Fungistatic A pesticide that prevents the development of fungal pathogens without killing them.

Fungus (Pl. Fungi) A group of organisms that lack chlorophyll and thus cannot produce its own food. Fungi live on dead or living plant or animal tissue. Fungi have threadlike structures known as hyphae that are collectively known as mycelium and analogous to the vegetative parts of plants. Instead of seeds, fungi produce a variety of sexual and asexual spores that account for fungal reproduction.

General-use Pesticide A pesticide that has been assessed not to harm the applicator or the environment to an unreasonable degree when used according to label directions, and thus may be purchased and used by laymen who are not certified to use restricted-use pesticides. Compare with restricted-use pesticide.

Hard Water A characteristic problem with many water sources in the world where there are high concentrations of dissolved salts (calcium, iron, magnesium) that adversely affect emulsion and dispersion properties of pesticides.

Herbicide A specific group of pesticides used to kill or inhibit plant growth; "weed killers."

Honeydew Liquid, rich in sugars, discharged from the anus of certain insects (soft scales, mealybugs, aphids and whitefly nymphs), usually noted by the growth of sooty mold fungi.

Host A plant species that provides some or all of the nutrients for a particular pest species.

Inert Ingredient Any ingredient of a product (pesticide) that does not add to the activity of the active component. In pesticide formulations, such inerts would be clay, sand, talc, liquid diluents, etc.

Infectious Disease A disease that can be spread from one plant to another because it is caused by a living organism. Also known as a biotic or parasitic disease.

Inoculum The pathogen or its infectious parts (spores, mycelium) that can cause plant disease.

Insect A small invertebrate that has the body divided into three regions: the head, thorax and abdomen. The thorax is divided into three segments, each bearing a pair of legs. The first two segments of the thorax of adults usually each bear a pair of wings.

Insecticide A chemical that is lethal to insects.

Integrated Pest Management (IPM) The use of all available control techniques including biological, chemical, cultural and physical into a customized pest management program for a specific crop or crop sequence.

Invertebrate An animal without a backbone, such as an insect, mite, nematode, snail or spider.

Larva (Pl. Larvae) The immature stages, between the egg and pupa, of an insect having a complete metamorphosis. An immature stage differing radically from the adult.

LC$_{50}$ The amount of a pesticide to kill 50

percent of a test animal population in a standard test when administered in air or water; normally expressed as milligrams (mg) of pesticide per liter of water or air.

LD_{50} The amount of a pesticide (administered orally or dermally) needed to kill 50 percent of a test animal population. This is expressed as milligrams (mg) of pesticide per kilogram (kg) of body weight of the test animal.

Leaf Spot An obvious area of diseased tissue on a leaf, variable in size, shape and color, that may be caused by various types of pathogens.

Life Cycle The complete succession of life stages of an organism (from being born to giving birth).

Microencapsulation A formulation process whereby a highly dangerous active ingredient is made less hazardous by dissolving the active in a solution of a polymer and then, through heat and chemical interaction, to seal the active into polymer-coated particles.

Mildews A group of plant diseases that characteristically exhibit a white mycelial growth of the causal fungus on the surfaces of infected plant parts (powdery mildews on both leaf surfaces, downy mildews on the lower leaf surface).

Mycelium (Pl. Mycelia) The vegetative body of a fungus composed of slender strands (hyphae).

Mycorrhiza (Pl. Mycorrhizae) A symbiotic association between certain fungi and roots of plants, literally "fungus root."

Nematicide A chemical that is lethal or strongly inhibitory to nematodes.

Nematodes Simple worms, lacking body segments, which have adapted themselves to many habitats. Those which are parasites of plants are generally small ($^1/_{100}$ to $^1/_8$ inch or 0.25 to 3.0 mm long) and colorless, and feed on plant cells through a sharp, needle-like stylet which resembles a hypodermic needle.

Necrosis The disintegration or death of plant cells, tissues or parts (regardless of cause) that is characterized by a brown, black or white discoloration of that portion of the plant.

NIOSH The National Institute for Occupational Safety and Health that acts as a review and certification organization for such safety equipment as respirators.

Noninfectious Disease A disease incapable of spreading from one plant to another since it is caused by nonliving, environmental factors. Also known as abiotic or nonparasitic disease.

Nonparasitic Disease A disease caused by nonliving agents such as environmental factors that cannot enter into a parasitic relationship with a host plant. Also known as abiotic or noninfectious diseases.

Parasite An organism that resides on or in another organism and derives some or all of its nutrients from the host organism. Parasitic organisms can be either obligate (surviving only on or in a living organism) or facultative (surviving on live or dead organisms).

Pathogen Any living agent capable of causing plant disease. Most pathogens are parasites but some are saprophytes.

Pest Any organism that can cause disease or injury to plants or plant products.

Pesticide A chemical agent that destroys pests (pathogens, insects, nematodes, weeds).

Physical Compatibility When two or more chemical ingredients can be mixed together in a dissolved or suspended state without immediate and persistent physical separation like oil on water.

Phytotoxicity Chemical injury to a plant; often used to describe the adverse effects of a pesticide on a particular plant.

Poison This term on a pesticide label (with the accompanying skull and crossbones) denotes a highly toxic pesticide with an oral LD_{50} of less than 50 mg/kg and a dermal LD_{50} less than 200 mg/kg. Follow all label precautions *precisely* and wear specified protective clothing and other equipment at all times during use.

Powdery Mildew Common name for one of a group of fungal pathogens that form a dusty or powdery white growth on the surfaces of plant parts.

PPB Abbreviation for parts per billion; analogous to 1 inch in 16,000 miles.

PPM Abbreviation for parts per million; analogous to 1 inch in 16 miles.

Protectant A pesticide applied to a plant surface prior to infection by a pathogen in an effort to prevent such infection.

Residual The attribute of a pesticide to remain at levels toxic to target pests on plant surfaces or in the soil or plant tissues for a period of time (days to weeks).

Resistance The inherent qualities of a host plant which enable that plant to resist the action of a pathogenic organism, which may operate at varying levels of efficiency. Also, a category of disease control utilizing host plant genetic resistance.

Restricted-use Pesticide A pesticide that is viewed as potentially harmful to applicator and/or environment even when used as directed. The following statement appears on such a pesticide: "Restricted use pesticide for purchase and use only by certified applicators or by persons under their direct supervision."

Ringspot A viral disease symptom that exhibits chlorotic or necrotic ring patterns (with green centers) on plant tissue.

Rot A state of putrefaction or decay.

Rust The common name for a group of diseases that are incited by rust fungi. These pathogens have complex life cycles and may need to infect more than one host to complete their life cycles. The common name is from the rust colored spore discharge from affected plant parts.

Soluble Powder (SP) A powder formulation of pesticide that dissolves to form a solution in water.

Sooty Mold Darkly pigmented fungi that feed on honeydew secreted by such insects as aphids, mealy bugs, scales and whiteflies and thereby produce a sooty covering on leaves, stems and fruit.

Spreader-stickers These are ingredients added to pesticide formulations or into a tank-mix combination that cause the spray film to better cover and adhere to the solid plant surface than if the pesticide were used alone.

Systemic A term applying to a disease type or kind of pesticide. Systemic diseases are those in which the pathogen becomes generally distributed throughout the plant as with bacterial crown gall or a viral disease. A systemic pesticide is one which is absorbed and moves within a plant.

Virus Microscopic pathogens, usually disseminated by insect vectors or through plant propagules, seeds or on workers' hands or equipment.

Warning This term on a pesticide label denotes a moderately toxic pesticide with an oral LD_{50} range of 50 to 500 mg/kg and a dermal LD_{50} of 200 to 1000 mg/kg. Protective clothing and devices should be used since harmful quantities of this pesticide can be absorbed through the skin.

Water Dispersible (WDG) A water dispersible granule formulation of a pesticide that offers advantages over wettable powder types. It creates less dust during loading/mixing operations, does not "pack" or "settle" in transit and is easier to measure than wettable powders.

Wettable Powder (WP) A formulation of pesticide that is easily wetted by water to go into suspension.

(Reprinted with modifications from *A Plant Protection Glossary for Master Gardeners.* Revision 4, 1997, Florida Cooperative Extension Service, University of Florida, Gainesville, Florida.)

Resources for Identifying Orchid Ailments

ORCHIDISTS CONFRONTED WITH pest and disease problems on their orchid plants and flowers can obtain a diagnosis and possible solutions from several sources.

Growers and Societies

Two resources within the orchid community are commercial growers and local orchid societies. Employees and members are often willing to examine an infected specimen and suggest controls. Ask an orchid-nursery employee or officers of a local orchid society to determine if it is permissible to bring an infected plant to a nursery or meeting or show. If it is, slip the plant, or the infected part, into a paper or plastic bag, or wrap it in newspaper, to prevent contaminating other orchids. (Avoid leaving a bagged orchid in a car during the heat of summer or on a cold winter day or it will be cooked or chilled, respectively.) Information on local Affiliated Societies of the American Orchid Society, which hold meetings and orchid shows, is available from the American Orchid Society, 16700 AOS Lane, Delray Beach, Florida 33446-4351 (telephone 561-404-2000; fax 561-404-2100; e-mail TheAOS@aos.org). A listing of Affiliated Societies and commercial growers is available on the World Wide Web at the Society's Web site, www.aos.org.

County Cooperative Extension Service

Many states have County Cooperative Extension Service agents that will make identifications at no cost or for a nominal fee. They are often listed under the name of your county in the white pages of the telephone directory. If there is none near you, an alternative is to mail the infected orchid to the central extension office in your state. Each of these offices can direct orchidists to a County Cooperative Extension Office. If it is necessary to mail a sample for examination, ask for packing and mailing instructions so the symptoms will not be altered during shipping. Paper is recommended; avoid plastic, which often causes plant tissue to rot during transit. Botanical gardens and horticultural societies may also be able to offer advice or recommend sources capable of identifying orchid ailments.

To receive an accurate and detailed diagnosis, submit a sample of the plant and/or flower and a written description that gives:

- the plant's name
- where the plant was obtained
- whether it is a seedling or a flowering-size specimen
- day the sample was colleccted
- when the problem was noticed
- which parts of the plant are affected
- if the plant is grown indoors or outdoors (describe the location)
- soil and watering conditions
- exposure (amount of light received)

Video

The American Orchid Society offers an educational video, *Orchid Pests and Diseases* (68 minutes, VHS), which shows how to distinguish cultural problems from symptoms of damage caused by an assortment of pests, bacteria, fungi and viruses. Copies are available for sale through the Orchid Emporium Gift Shop (telephone 561-404-2061; e-mail TheAOS @aos.org; Web site www.aos.org).

Ailment Identification Services

This list of university related plant disease clinics was compiled by Gail Ruhl,

Senior Plant Disease Diagnostician, Department of Botany and Plant Pathology, Purdue University. Compiled in 2005, a current listing can be found on the World Wide Web at http://apsnet.org/directories/univ_diagnosticians.asp. An asterisk (*) indicates a service center obtained from another source. In addition to the following resources, many states also have diagnostic labs associated with their State Department of Agriculture, or with United States Department of Agriculture (USDA) Research facilities. It is recommended you contact your local county extension office for sample submission procedures to the diagnostic lab. A listing of Plant Pathology and Nematology Specialists on the World Wide Web, jointly maintained by the USDA and the American Phytopathological Society, can be found at www.apsnet.org/directories/extension/top.asp

Alabama

Plant Disease Clinic
ALFA Agricultural Services Bldg.
961 S. Donahue Drive
Department of Entomology and
    Plant Pathology
Auburn University
Auburn, Alabama 36849-5624
Tel 334-844-5508 (-5507)
Fax 334-844-4072
Contact Jacqueline Mullen
E-mail jmullen.@acesag.auburn.edu
or mullejm@auburn.edu

Plant Diagnostic Lab at Birmingham
C. Beaty Hanna Hort. And Environ. Center
2612 Lane Park Road
Birmingham, AL 35223-1802
Phone: 205 879-6964 ext. 18
Fax: 205 414-3906
Contact: James Jacobi
E-mail: jjacobi@aces.edu
jacobjc@auburn.edu

Alaska

Dept. of Plant, Animal and Soil Sciences
University of Alaska
Agricultural Forestry Experimental Station
Fairbanks, Alaska 99775-7200
Tel 907-474-7431
Fax 907-474-7439
Contact Jenifer Huang McBeath
E-mail ffjhm@uaf.edu or
    ffjhm@aurora.alaska.edu

Arizona

Extension Plant Pathologist
University of Arizona
Yuma Agriculture Center
6425 West 8th Street
Yuma, Arizona 85364
Tel 928-726-0458
Contact Mike Matheron
E-mail matheron@ag.arizona.edu

Extension Plant Pathologist
Department of Plant Pathology
Forbes Building 204
University of Arizona
Tucson, Arizona 85721
Tel 928-626-2681
Fax 928-621-9290
Contact Mary Olsen
E-mail molsen@ag.arizona.edu
Web site http:/ag.arizona.edu/PLP/plptext

Arkansas

Plant Disease Clinic
Lonoke Agricultural Center
PO Box 357
Highway 70 East
Lonoke, Arkansas 72086
Tel 501-676-3124
Fax 501-676-7847
Contact Stephen Vann
E-mail svann@uaex

California

Contact your local county farm advisor or extension specialist at your nearest university.

Colorado
Plant Diagnostic Clinic
Jefferson County Extension
15200 West 6th Avenue, Suite C
Golden, Colorado 80401
Tel 303-271-6620
Fax 303-271-6644
Contact Mary Small
E-mail msmall@co.jefferson.co.us or
    jefferso@coop.ext.colostate.edu

Identification and Diagnostic Service
342-A General Services Building
Department of Bioagriculture Sciences
    and Pest Management
Colorado State University
Fort Collins, Colorado 80523-1177
Tel 970-491-6950
E-mail idlab@ceres.agsci.colostate.edu

Plant Diagnostic Clinic
E 215 Plant Sciences Building
Department of Bioagriculture Sciences
    and Pest Management
Colorado State University
Fort Collins, Colorado 80523-1177
Tel 970-491-6950
Contact Tamela Blun
E-mail plantlab@lamar.colostate.edu

Connecticut
Contact your local County Farm Advisor
or Extension Specialist at your nearest
university.

Delaware
Extension Plant Pathologist
Plant and Soil Sciences Department
151 Townsend Hall
University of Delaware
531 S College Avenue
Newark, Delaware 19717-1303
Tel 302-831-4865
Fax 302-831-0605
Contact Robert Mulrooney
E-mail bobmul@udel.edu

Florida
Florida Extension Plant Disease Clinic
Building U.F. 78 Mowry Road
PO Box 110830
University of Florida
Gainesville, Florida 32611-0830
Tel 352-392-1795
Fax 352-392-3438
Contact Richard E. Cullen/Bob McGovern
E-mail pdc@ifas.ufl.edu
Web site http://plantpath.ifas.ufl.edu

Regional State Labs:
Florida Extension Plant Diagnostic Clinic
IFAS/NFREC
155 Research Road
Quincy, Florida 32351
Tel 850-875-7140
Fax 850-875-7188
Contact Timur Momol and H. Dankers
E-mail tmomol@ifas.ufl.edu
Web site
http://www.jmok.ufl.edu/plant/index. htm

Florida Extension Plant Disease Clinic
Southwest Florida Research and
    Education Center
2686 State Road 29 North
Immokalee, Florida 34142-9515
Tel 941-658-3400 (-3429)
Fax 941-751-3469
Contact P. Roberts and R. Urs
E-mail pdr@gnv.ifas.ufl.edu

Florida Extension Plant Disease Clinic
Southwest Florida Research and
    Education Center
2686 State Road 29 North
Immokalee, Florida 34142-9515
Tel 239-658-3400
Fax 239-751-3469
Contact Pamela Roberts and Rrama Urs
E-mail pdr@mail.ifas.ufl.edu
Web site
http://www.imok.ufl.edu/plant/index.htm

Florida Extension Plant Disease Clinic
Tropical Research and Education Center

18905 Southwest 280th Street
Homestead, Florida 33031
Tel 305-246-7001, ext. 270
Fax 305-246-7003
Contact A. J. Palmateer
E-mail ajpalmateer@ifas.ufl.edu
Web site http://trecclinic.ifas.ufl.edu

Georgia
Extension Plant Disease Clinic
 Department of Plant Pathology
Miller Plant Sciences Building
University of Georgia
Athens, Georgia 30602
Tel 706-542-9140
Fax 706-542-4102
Contact Jean Williams-Woodward
E-mail jwoodwar@uga.edu

Hawaii
Plant Disease Clinic
Agricultural Diagnostic Service Center
 1910 East-West Road
Sherman Lab 134
Honolulu, Hawaii 96822
Phone 808-956-6706
Fax 808-956-2592
E-mail adsc@ctahr.hawaii.edu
Web site http://www2.ctahr.hawaii.edu/adsc

Idaho
Extension Plant Pathologist
Kimberly Diagnostic Lab
University of Idaho
Research and Extension Center
3793 North 3600 East
Kimberly, Idaho 83341
Tel 208-423-6621
Fax 208-423-6559
Contact Carl Strausbaugh
E-mail carl@uidaho.edu
Web site
http://www.uidaho.edu/ag/plantdisease/

Extension Plant Pathologist
University of Idaho
Research and Extension Center
29603 University of Idaho Lane
Parma, Idaho 83660-6699
Tel 208-722-6701 or Ext. 218

Fax 208-722-6708
Contact Krishna Mohan
E-mail kmohan@uidaho.edu
Nematology contact Saad Hafez

Illinois
May–September:
Plant Clinic
1401 West Saint Mary's Road
University of Illinois
Urbana, Illinois 61802
Tel 217-333-0519
Contact Nancy Pataky
E-mail npataky@uiuc.edu
Web site
http://plantclinic.cropsci.uiuc.edu

October–March:
N-533 Turner Hall
1102 South Goodwin Avenue
University of Illinois
Urbana, Illinois 61801
Tel 217-333-2478
Fax 217-333-1289
Contact Nancy Pataky
E-mail npataky@uiuc.edu

Indiana
Plant and Pest Diagnostic Laboratory
Purdue University
LSPS 101
915 West State Street
West Lafayette, Indiana 47907-2054
Tel 765-494-7071
Fax 765-494-3958
Contact Karen Rane
Tel 765-494-5821
E-mail rane@purdue.edu
Contact Gail Ruhl
Tel 765-494-4641
E-mail ruhl@purdue.edu
Web site www.ppdl.purdue.edu

Iowa
Plant Disease Clinic
Department of Plant Pathology
323 Bessey Hall
Iowa State University
Ames, Iowa 50011

Tel 515-294-0581
Fax 515-294-9420
Contact Paula Flynn or
   Christine Engelbrecht
E-mail pflynn@iastate.edu or
cengel@iastate.edu
Web site www.isuplantdiseaseclinic.org

Kansas
Plant Disease Diagnostic Lab
Extension Plant Pathology
4032 Throckmorton Hall
Kansas State University
Manhattan, Kansas 66506-5504
Tel 785-532-5810
Fax 785-532-5692
Contact Judith O'Mara
E-mail omara@plantpath.ksu.edu
Web site www.oznet.ksu.edu/path.ext/

Kentucky
Central and Eastern Kentucky:
Plant Disease Diagnostic Lab
Department of Plant Pathology
S305 Agricultural Science Center - North
University of Kentucky
Lexington, Kentucky 40546-0091
Tel 859-257-8949
Fax 859-323-1961
Contact Julie Beale
E-mail jbeale@uky.edu.

Western Kentucky:
Plant Disease Diagnostic Lab
Department of Plant Pathology
University of Kentucky Research and
   Education Center
PO Box 469
1205 Hopkinsville Street
Princeton, Kentucky 42445
Tel 270-365-7541 Ext. 228
Fax 270-365-2667
Contact Paul Bachi
E-mail pbachi@uky.edu
Web site www.ca.uky.edu/agcollege
/plantpathology/PPAExten/ppaext.html

Louisiana
Plant Disease Diagnostic Clinic,

Department of Plant Pathology and
   Crop Physiology
LSU Agricultural Center
Baton Rouge, Louisiana 70803
Tel 225-578-5724
Fax 225-578-1415
Contact Charles Overstreet
E-mail coverstreet@agctr.lsu.edu

Maine
Pest Management Office
Cooperative Extension
University of Maine
491 College Avenue
Orono, Maine 04473-1295
Tel 207-581-3880
Fax 207-581-3881
Contact Bruce Watt
E-mail bwatt@umext.maine.edu
Web site http://pmo.umext.maine.edu

Maryland
Plant Diagnostic Laboratory
Department of Entomology
University of Maryland
3171 Plant Sciences Building
College Park, Maryland 20742-4454
Tel 301-405-1611
(-3913) Fax 301-314-9290
Contact Ethel Dutky
E-mail edutky@umd.edu
Web site www.plantclinic.umd.edu

Home and Garden Information Center*
12005 Homewood Road
Ellicott City, Maryland 21042
Tel 410-531-5556
Maryland residents only 1-800-342-2507
Web site www.hgic.umd.edu

Massachusetts
No disease diagnostic service is offered
by a public agency to homeowners.

Michigan
Diagnostic Services
101 CIPS
Michigan State University
East Lansing, Michigan 48824-1311
Tel 517-353-3504

Fax 517-432-0899
Contact Jan Byrne
E-mail byrnejm@msu.edu
Web site www.cips.msu.edu/diagnostics

Minnesota
For Homeowners:
The Yard and Garden Clinic has closed.
Please see http://www.extension.umn.edu/
projects/yardandgarden/ or call
612 624-4771 for more info.

For Commercial Growers:
Plant Disease Clinic
Department of Plant Pathology
495 Borlaug Hall
1991 Upper Buford Circle
University of Minnesota
St. Paul, Minnesota 55108
Tel 612-625-1275
Fax 612-625-9728
Contact Sandra Gould
E-mail gould001@umn.edu
Web site www.plpa.agri.umn.edu/extension/
plantdiseaseclinic.htm

Mississippi
Plant Pathology Lab
Room 9, Bost Extension Center
Box 9655
Mississippi State,
Mississippi 39762-9655
Tel 662-325-2146
Fax 662-325-8407
Contact Clarissa Balbalian
E-mail cbalbali@ext.msstate.edu
Web site www.msstate.edu/dept/
extensionplantclinics

Missouri
Extension Plant Diagnostic Clinic
23 Mumford Hall
University of Missouri
Columbia, Missouri 65211
Tel 573-882-3019
Fax 573-884-4288
Contact Simeon Wright
E-mail wrights@missouri.edu
Web site http://agebb.missouri.edu/pdc/

Montana
Plant Disease Clinic
119 Ag Bioscience Facility
Department of Plant Sciences and Plant
Pathology
Montana State University
Bozeman, Montana 59717-3150
Tel 406-994-5150
Fax 406-994-7600
Contact Jack Riesselman
E-mail jhr@montana.edu

Nebraska
Plant and Pest Diagnostic Clinic
Department of Plant Pathology
448 Plant Sciences
University of Nebraska
Lincoln, Nebraska 68583-0722
Tel 402-472-2559
Fax 402-472-2853
Contact Jennifer Chaky
E-mail jchaky2@unl.edu

Nevada
No university disease diagnostic services
are available.

New Hampshire
Plant Diagnostic Lab
38 College Road
G37 Spaulding Hall
Plant Biology Department
University of New Hampshire
Durham, New Hampshire 03824
Tel 603-862-3841
Fax 603-862-2717
Contact Cheryl Smith
E-mail cheryl.smith@unh.edu
Web site http://ceinfo.unh.edu/Agric/
AGPDTS/PlantH.htm

New Jersey
Plant Diagnostic Lab
Rutgers University
PO Box 550
Milltown, New Jersey 08850
Tel 732-932-9140
Fax 732-932-1270
Contact Rich Buckley

E-mail clinic@aesop.rutgers.edu
Web site www.rce.rutgers.edu/plant
diagnosticlab

New Mexico
Plant Diagnostic Clinic
PO Box 30003, MSC. 3AE
Plant Sciences
Cooperative Extension Service
New Mexico State University
Las Cruces, New Mexico 88003
Tel 505-646-1621
Fax 505-646-8085
Contact Natalie Goldberg
E-mail ngoldber@nmsu.edu

New York
Homeowner and Commercial:
Plant Disease Diagnostic Clinic
Department of Plant Pathology
334 Plant Science Building
Cornell University
Ithaca, New York 14853-4203
Tel 607-255-7850
Fax 607-255-4471
Contact Karen Snover-Clift
E-mail kls13@cornell.edu
Contact Sandra Jensen-Tracy
E-mail slj2@cornell.edu

Commercial Ornamental Samples Only:
Long Island Horticultural Research and
Extension Center
Cornell University 3059 Sound Avenue
Riverhead, New York 11901
Tel 631-727-3595
Fax 631-727-3611
Contact Margery Daughtrey
E-mail mld9@cornell.ed

North Carolina
Plant Disease and Insect Clinic
Campus Box 7211
Room 1104 Williams Hall
North Carolina State University
Raleigh, North Carolina 27695-7211
Tel 919-515-3619
Fax 919-515-7716
Contact Tom Creswell

E-mail tom_creswell@ncsu.edu
Web site www/mcsi/edi[doc

North Dakota
Plant Diagnostic Lab
NDSU Plant Diagnostic Lab
PO Box 5012
North Dakota State University
Fargo, North Dakota 58105
Tel 701-231-7854
Fax 701-231-7851
Contact Cheryl Biller
E-mail diaglab@ndsuext.nodak.edu

Ohio
C. Wayne Ellett Plant and Pest Diagnostic
Clinic
110 Kottman Hall
2021 Coffey Road
The Ohio State University
Columbus, Ohio 43210-1087
Tel 614-292-5006
Fax 614-292-4455
Contact Nancy Taylor
E-mail taylor.8@osu.edu
Web site http://ppdc.osu.edu/

Oklahoma
Plant Disease Diagnostic Lab
Department of Entomology and
Plant Pathology
127 Noble Research Center
Oklahoma State University
Stillwater, Oklahoma 74078
Tel 405-744-9961
Fax 405-744-7373
Contact Richard Grantham
E-mail entoman@okstate.edu
Web site http://entoplp.okstate.edu/pddl

Oregon
Plant Disease Clinic
Extension Plant Pathology
Cordley Hall, Room 1089
Oregon State University
Corvallis, Oregon 97331-2903
Tel 541-737-3472
Fax 541-737-2412
Contact Melodie Putnam
E-mail putnamm@bcc.orst.eduPlant

Plant Pathology Lab
H.A.R.E.C.
Oregon State University
PO Box 105
Hermiston, Oregon 97838
Tel 541-567-8321
Fax 541-567-2240
Contact Philip Hamm
E-mail philip.b.hamm@orst.edu

Pennsylvania
Plant Disease Clinic
220 Buckhout Laboratory
Pennsylvania State University
University Park, Pennsylvania 16802
Tel 814-865-2204
Fax 814-863-7217
Contact John Peplinski
E-mail jdp3@psu.edu

Rhode Island
URI Plant Protection Clinic
University of Rhode Island
CE Education Center
3 East Alumni Avenue
Kingston, Rhode Island 02881-0804
Tel 401-874-2967 (-2900)
Fax 401-874-5826
Contact David B. Wallace
E-mail ceec@etal.uri.edu
For Commercial Samples:
Cooperative Extension Service
University of Rhode Island
C.E. Center
Kingston, Rhode Island 02881
Tel 401-874-2900
Web site www.uri.edu/ce/plantclinic

South Carolina
Clemson University
Agricultural Service Laboratory
Plant Problem Clinic
171 Old Cherry Road
Clemson, South Carolina 29634-0114
Tel 864-656-3125
Fax 864-656-2069
Contact James Blake
E-mail jblake@clemson.edu
Web site www.clemson.edu/agrsrvlb

South Dakota
Plant Disease Clinic
Department of Plant Science
South Dakota State University
PO Box 2108 PSB 119
Brookings, South Dakota 57007-1090
Tel 605-688-5545
Fax 605-688-4024
Contact Kim Maxson-Stein
E-mail kimberly.stein@ur.sdstate.edu
Web site http://plantsci.sdstate.edu/
planthealth/PDCclinic.html

Tennessee
Plant and Pest Diagnostic Center
University of Tennessee
5201 Marchant Drive
Nashville, Tennessee 37211-5112
Tel 615-832-6802 Fax
615-781-2568
Contact Tom Stebbins and Alan Windham
E-mail tstebbins@utk.edu or
awindham@utk.edu
Web site http://web.utk.edu/~extepp

Texas
Texas Plant Disease Diagnostic Lab
Texas A&M University
1500 Research Parkway, Suite A130
College Station, Texas 77843-2589
Tel 979-845-8032
Fax 979-845-6499
Contact Larry Barnes
E-mail lbarnes@tamu.edu
Web site http://plantdiseaselab.tamu.edu

Utah
Plant Pest Diagnostic Lab
Department of Biology
Utah State University
Logan, Utah 84322-5305
Tel 435-797-2435
Fax 435-797-1575
Contact Karen Flint or Alan Roe
E-mail alanrbiology@usu.edu
Web site: http://extension.usu.edu/plantpath

Vermont
Plant Diagnostic Clinic
Department of Plant and Soil Science

University of Vermont
235 Hills Building
Burlington, Vermont 05405-0086
Tel 802-656-0493
Fax 802-656-4656
Contact Ann Hazelrigg
E-mail ann.hazelrigg@uvm.edu
Web site http://pss.uvm.edu/pd/pdc

Virginia
Plant Disease Clinic and Nematode Assay
  Lab
106 Price Hall
Department of Plant Pathology,
  Physiology and Weed Science
VPI and SU
Blacksburg, Virginia 24061-0331
Tel 540-231-6758
Fax 540-231-7477 (-3221)
Contact Mary Ann Hansen or Nina Hopkins
E-mail clinic@vt.edu
Web site www.ppws.vt.edu~clinic/

Washington
Plant Diagnostic Clinic
WSU-Puyallup Research and Extension
  Center
7612 Pioneer Way East
Puyallup, Washington 98371-4998
Tel 253-445-4582
Fax 253-445-4569
Contact Jenny Glass
E-mail jennyglass@wsu.edu
Web site www.puyallup.wsu.edu/
  plantclinic/index.html

West Virginia
Plant Disease Diagnostic Clinic
414 Brooks Hall
Downtown Campus
West Virginia University
Morgantown, West Virginia 26506
Tel 304-293-3911, Ext. 2226
Fax 304-293-2872
Contact John F. Baniecki
E-mail banieck@wvu.edu

Wisconsin
Plant Disease Diagnostic Clinic
Department of Plant Pathology

1630 Linden Drive
University of Wisconsin-Madison
Madison, Wisconsin 53706-1598
Tel 608-262-2863
Fax 608-263-2626
Contact Brian Hudelson
E-mail bdh@plantpath.wisc.edu
Web site www.plantpath.wisc.edu/pddc

Wyoming
Extension Plant Pathology Laboratory
Department of Plant Sciences
University of Wyoming
PO Box 3354
Laramie, Wyoming 82071-3354
Tel 307-766-5083
Fax 307-766-5549
Contact Raina Spence
E-mail rspence@uwyo.edu or briere@
  uwyo.edu

CANADA
Ontario
Pest Diagnostic Clinic
Laboratory Services Division
University of Guelph
95 Stone Road West
Guelph, Ontario, Canada N1H 8J7
Tel 519-767-6256 (-6299)
Fax 519-767-6240
Contact Marc Sabrouin
Tel 519-767-6227
E-mail msabouri@lsd.uoguelph.ca or
  pdc@lsd.uoguelph.ca

World Wide Web Sites
The following links represent some of
the on-line information resources dealing
with pests and diseases that affect
orchids.

aos.org
The American Orchid Society's Web site
offers basic information about orchid ail-
ment identification and care, with a trou-
ble-shooting section as well as information on culture and types to grow.
www.aos.org

First Rays Orchids

Several useful pages are listed under "All Kinds of Free Information." Two of these pages (see links below) offer information about various pests as well as some home remedies for controlling them.
www.firstrays.com/pests.htm
www.firstrays.com/remedies.htm

GT Orchid Lab

The "Virus Links" page offers a great deal of information about orchid viruses.
http://personal.alt.bellsouth.net/g/e/geotan1/virus.htm

Integrated Plant Protection Center

Oregon State University's Web site lists a variety of topics affecting many different types of plants, some of which is applicable to orchids. www.ippc.orst.edu

North Carolina State University

The Insect and Related Pests of Flowers and Foliage Plants site covers important, common, and potential pests in the southeastern United States.
http://ipm.ncsu.edu/AG136/ncstate.html
http://ipm.ncsu.edu/AG136/ncstate.html

Pesticide.Net

Maintained by the law firm of Wright & Sielaty and the scientific and regulatory consultants at ChemReg Int'l, this user-supported library contains news, information and resources on conventional, biological, biochemical and antimicrobial pesticides. This continuously updated pesticide-related news and regulatory information is available for free access for two weeks after being added to the site. After two weeks, it is available for unrestricted research and reference via subscription for $39.95 per quarter or $129.95 per year, and it is free to public-sector personnel. www.pesticide.net research and reference via subscription for $39.95 per quarter or $129.95 per year, and it is free to public-sector personnel. www.pesticide.net

South Dakota State University and the South Dakota Orchid Society

The orchid pests page provides information about various pests, methods of control, and links to other handy on-line pest-information Web sites. http://nathist.sdstate.edu/orchids/Pests/pests.htm

Addendum

Orchid Blossom Midge [*Contarinia aculipennis*]

The orchid blossom midge is a polyphagous cecidomyiid reported and described from Hawaii (Felt, 1933). In 1992, unopened flower buds of *Dendrobium* spp. were exhibiting damage from the larvae of this pest in central and southern Florida. Each bud contained from five to 30 small white larvae feeding on the bud, and moving freely among the flower parts (Gagné, 1995). When the larvae are fully developed they drop to the soil where they burrow into the soil and pupate. When larvae are on the soil surface they may jump several centimeters by tightly curling their bodies and quickly uncurling (Gagné, 1995). This behavior may help in identification. Adults will emerge about three weeks later.

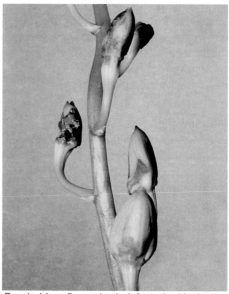

Dendrobium flower buds infested with the larvae of orchid blossom midge, *Contarinia maculipennis*.

The adults appear as small flies with long banded legs, large eyes, long antennae, and spotted wings (Gagné, 1995). The adult wingspan is about ¹/₈ inch (2.5 to 3 mm).

Larvae similar to *C. maculipennis* have been intercepted at United States ports of entry on *Dendrobium* spp. orchids shipped from Cambodia, Japan and Thailand (Gagné, 1995).

Control tactics have not been fully investigated, but destruction of infested buds as a sanitary measure will undoubtedly help. Because the larvae enter the soil to pupate, pesticide applications to the soil (pot media) could be beneficial.
— *Avas B. Hamon, PhD.*

References

Felt, E.P. 1933. A hibiscus bud midge new to Hawaii. *Proceedings of the Hawaiian Entomological Society* 41:87–89.

Gagné, R.J. 1995. *Contarinia maculipennis* (Diptera: Cecidomyiidae), a polyphagous pest newly reported for North America. *Bulletin of Entomological Research* 85:209–214.

Contributors

Authors

Harry C. Burnett, PhD, Plant Pathologist (Deceased), Division of Plant Industry, Florida Department of Agriculture and Consumer Services, Cowperthwaite Building, 3027 Lake Alfred Road, Winter Haven, Florida 33880.

R. A. Dunn, PhD, Professor and Extension Nematologist, Entomology and Nematology Department, PO Box 110640, Institute of Food and Agricultural Sciences, University of Florida, Gainesville, Florida 32611.

Avas B. Hamon, PhD, Taxonomic Entomologist (Retired), Florida Department of Agriculture and Consumer Services, Division of Plant Industry, PO Box 147100, Gainesville, Florida 32614.

Roger H. Lawson, PhD, Research Leader (Retired), Floral and Nursery Plants Research Unit, USDA, Agricultural Research Service, Beltsville Agricultural Research Center, Beltsville, Maryland 20705.

James F. Price, PhD, University of Florida Food and Agricultural Sciences, Gulf Coast Research and Education Center, 5007 60th Street East, Bradenton, Florida 34203.

Thomas J. Sheehan, PhD, Professor Emeritus of Environmental Horticulture, Department of Environmental Horticulture, University of Florida, Gainesville, Florida 32611.

Donald E. Short, PhD, Extension Entomologist, Institute of Food and Agricultural Services, University of Florida, Gainesville, Florida 32611.

Gary W. Simone, PhD, Extension Plant Pathologist, PO Box 110830, Institute of Food and Agricultural Services, University of Florida, Gainesville, Florida 32611.

Photographers

Page numbers only are given where a photographer has supplied all the photographs for a particular page. Directionals are given when photographs of two or more photographers appear on the same page.

Greg Allikas Front Cover (all except top inset) and Back Cover, 1
Stephen R. Batchelor 4 (right), 5 (right), 6, 11 (left), 13, 15, 16 (right)
Bob Benson 18
James Brasch 7, 8
Charles Marden Fitch Front Cover (top inset), 2, 9, 11 (right), 12, 16 (left), 17, 20
FDACS-DPI, Courtesy of 37–48
Terry O'Driscoll 77–90, 92–93
Thomas J. Sheehan, PhD 4 (left), 21
Gary W. Simone, PhD, and Harry C. Burnett, PhD 50, 52–53, 55–69
G.J. Steck 120
Susan M. Stephenson 5 (left)
M. van de Vrie 24–25

Production Staff

Editor James B. Watson
Art Director David Wong
Assistant Editor Susan Jones
Production Assistant Jane Mengel
Contributing Editors Sylvia Wood, Paul J. Johnson, PhD

"Physiological Disorders of Orchids" on pages 4–21 is a revision of the original chapter written by O. Wesley Davidson, PhD.

Index

Entries indexed include major subject headings and binomials in italics. Page numbers in boldface indicate illustrations.